Contents

UNIVERSITY

AutoCAD Worked Examples

A. Yarwood

Registered Developer and Master Developer with Autodesk Ltd
Member of the Autodesk Developer Network

Longman

The author wishes to acknowledge his gratitude
for the help given to him by Autodesk Ltd

Pearson Education Limited
Edinburgh Gate, Harlow
Essex CM20 2JE, England
and Associated Companies throughout the world

First published 2000

British Library Cataloguing in Publication Data
A catalogue entry for this title is available from the British Library

ISBN 0-582-42490-9

Set by 35 in 10/13pt Melior
Printed in Singapore

List of plates

Preface

Autodesk first introduced AutoCAD in 1982, and since then have released a number of updates and new versions. At the time of writing AutoCAD 2000 is the latest. Below is a short history showing the years in which the various releases were published. This book includes worked examples and exercises in 2D technical drawing and 3D solid model creation designed to be constructed using AutoCAD Release 12 to AutoCAD 2000 working in Windows 95/98/NT.

Release 1   (1982) – Version 1.00, Version 1.10 (DOS version)
Release 2   (April 1983) – Version 1.20 (dimensioning introduced)
Release 3   (August 1983) – Version 1.30
Release 4   (October 1983) – Version 1.4
Release 5   (1984) – Version 2.00
Release 6   (1985) – Version 2.10, Version 2.18
Release 7   (1986) – Version 2.50, Version 2.52
Release 8   (April 1987) – Version 2.60
Release 9   (September 1987)
Release 10 (1988) – 3D surface wireframes introduced
Release 11 (1990) – AME introduced
Release 12 (1993)
Release 13 (1996) – 3D data included with 2D data
Release 14 (1997) – Available only for use with Windows and NT
AutoCAD 2000 (1999)

Most operators using AutoCAD today will probably be using computers running AutoCAD Release 12, 13 or 14, or AutoCAD 2000, under Windows 95/98/NT.

In AutoCAD LT the methods of constructing 2D drawings are the same as those in AutoCAD. This means that the 2D examples given in this book are also suitable for operators using AutoCAD LT for Windows or AutoCAD LT 97, 98 or 2000.

One of the strengths of AutoCAD is that the basic methods for constructing simple 2D drawings have not changed significantly since the first release of the software. With the advent of Release 11, 3D solid drawings could also be produced on screen, provided the Advanced Modelling Extension (AME) software was used with Release 11 or Release 12. Release 13, Release 14 and AutoCAD 2000 incorporated the tools for 3D drawing with the 2D tools. The AutoCAD releases most likely to be in use today are Releases 12, 13 and 14, and AutoCAD 2000; the methods of constructing 3D models are similar in each.

This book includes worked AutoCAD examples and exercises. The 2D examples and exercises can be worked with almost any AutoCAD release. The 3D examples and exercises are only suitable for use with Release 12 (with AME loaded), Releases 13 and 14, and AutoCAD 2000.

Future releases of the software are expected to preserve the basic 2D drawing methods, and the basic methods of producing 3D models. This means that the contents of this book should also be suitable for use with later releases than AutoCAD 2000.

The more sophisticated possibilities of AutoCAD are not dealt with in this book. The book is aimed at the student, beginner or anyone new to using AutoCAD to produce technical drawings. Once the basic methods of operating the software have been mastered, more complex operations can easily be learned.

A. Yarwood

CHAPTER 1

Introduction

Glossary of terms used in this book

Click or *left-click*: Move the cursor (using the mouse) over a feature and press and release the left mouse button.

Right-click: Press and release the right mouse button. The same result can be achieved by pressing the **Return** or **Enter** key.

Double-click: Move the cursor over a feature and press and release the left mouse button twice in rapid succession.

Select: Move the cursor over a feature and press and release the left mouse button.

Pick: Move the cursor to a chosen position and press and release the left mouse button.

Drag: Move the cursor over a feature and press and keep down the left mouse while moving the mouse to a new position (then release the button).

Enter: Type in the given characters or figures using the keyboard.

Return: Press the **Return** or **Enter** key.

Objects: Lines, circles, etc. When objects are grouped together all the elements of the group can be treated as a single object.

Command line: Appears below the drawing area in an AutoCAD window as either a space (Release 12) or a separate window (later releases). The top line carries the word **Command:** and there is usually space for three lines of words or figures. Typed commands for constructing drawings are *entered* here.

Launching AutoCAD

It is assumed that the reader will know how to launch AutoCAD. If working at a school or college, it may be that when the computer is switched on the screen will show information about how to launch software.

When working in Windows 95/98/NT a *double-click* on the AutoCAD icon on the Windows desktop will launch the software.

Fig. 1.1 Windows desktop icons for different AutoCAD releases

Figure 1.1 shows the desktop icons for Releases 12, 13, 14, AutoCAD 2000 and LT 98, as they appear on my computer.

Running AutoCAD in Windows

Recent releases of AutoCAD – Release 14 and AutoCAD 2000 – have been designed to work only in Windows 95/98/NT. Prior to Release 14 versions of AutoCAD supported a variety of operating systems including MS-DOS; Release 12 was the first version to operate under Microsoft Windows.

The examples in this book dealing with 2D constructions are also suitable for use with any Windows' version of AutoCAD LT. Note that when using AutoCAD LT 3D construction capability is severely limited; AutoCAD LT is basically only a 2D program, with very limited 3D tools.

When using any of the Windows' versions, there are four common methods of calling tools (or commands). These are:

Entering the tool name (command name) at the command line (typing the name on the keyboard).
Entering an abbreviation for the tool name at the command line.
Selecting a tool icon from a toolbox (Release 12) or from a toolbar (Releases 13 to 2000).
Selecting a tool name from a drop-down menu.

In general, tool names and their abbreviations have not changed since Release 12, and icons representing tools are unchanged since Release 13. Also, although drop-down menus have needed to change because of the advances made in CAD technology, the basic tool names in the menus are the same throughout the Windows versions of AutoCAD. There have been many technological advances in CAD software programming: the ability to transfer data between drawings and databases; the ability to include bitmaps in drawings; the rapid development of methods to use the Internet to transfer drawing between computers anywhere in the world (from Release 14 onwards); the ability to open several drawings on screen and work on them at the same time (AutoCAD 2000). These advances have not changed basic methods of construction in the Windows' versions of AutoCAD.

Despite the changing appearance of AutoCAD, if the basic constructional methods are understood, it does not matter which version is in use. For more advanced operations, such as transferring drawings across the Internet, it will be necessary to use the later releases. In this book however, we are only concerned with the production of drawings on screen which can be transferred to paper via a printer or plotter.

The different appearances of AutoCAD

Figures 1.2–1.5 illustrate the appearance of the AutoCAD window for each of the versions from Release 12 to AutoCAD 2000.

AutoCAD Release 12 for Windows: When loaded into the computer the window appears on screen usually with a toolbox containing a number of tool icons. The command line at the bottom of the window is part of the AutoCAD window.

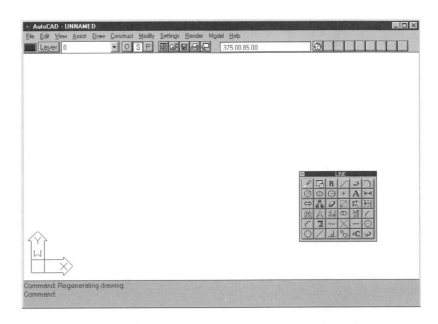

Fig. 1.2 AutoCAD Release 12 window

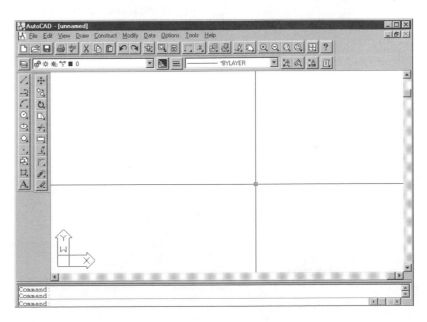

Fig. 1.3 AutoCAD Release 13 window

AutoCAD Release 13: Toolbars were first introduced with this release. Each toolbar carries tool icons for a particular set of operations. Usually the window opens with the **Draw** (general construction tools) and **Modify** (tools for modifying or editing) toolbars 'docked' against the left-hand side of the window and the **Standard** (frequently used tools such as opening and saving drawings, plotting, printing, etc.) and **Object Properties** (tools

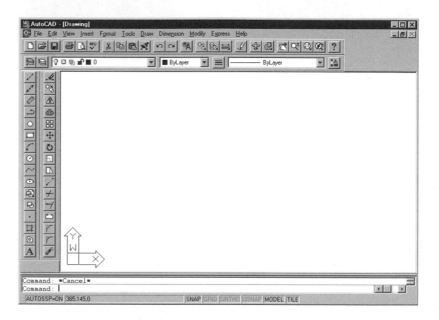

Fig. 1.4 AutoCAD Release 14 window

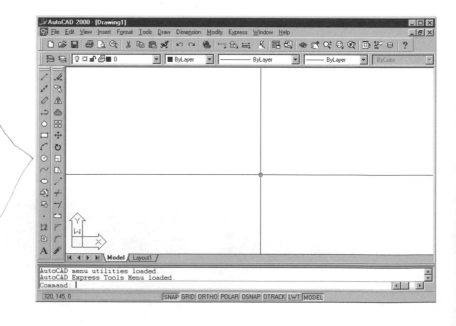

Fig. 1.5 AutoCAD 2000 window

for setting layers and colours) toolbars docked against the top of the window. Tool icons in these toolbars carry a number of 'flyouts' from which tools associated with a particular tool can be selected. The command line is in a separate window, which can be resized and moved just like any other window.

AutoCAD Release 14: The major difference in the appearance is that the toolbars carry very few flyouts. The same toolbars are docked against the left-hand and top edges of the window.

AutoCAD Release 2000: When first opened the window appears similar to that of Release 14. A careful examination of Figures 1.3 and 1.4 is needed to find the differences.

Tool icons

Figure 1.6 shows the differences between the toolbox of Release 12 and the toolbars of later releases.

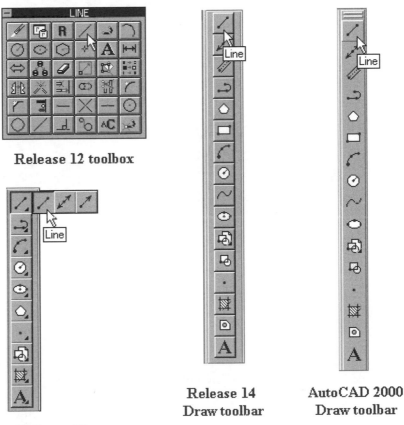

Release 12 toolbox

Release 13 Draw toolbar

Release 14 Draw toolbar

AutoCAD 2000 Draw toolbar

Fig. 1.6 Toolbox (Release 12) and toolbars (other releases)

In Release 12 when the cursor is moved over a tool icon, the name of that tool shows in the toolbox title bar.

In later releases 'tooltips' appear when the cursor is moved over a tool icon.

The look of the tool icons have not changed since Release 12.

Drop-down menus

Tools can be selected from drop-down menus. Figure 1.7 shows the **Draw** menus from the four AutoCAD releases. It will be noted that there are differences between the four menus. Despite these differences, the basic tools in the **Draw** menus – tools such as **Line**, **Polyline**, **Circle**, **Arc**, etc. – are available from the menu of any of the releases.

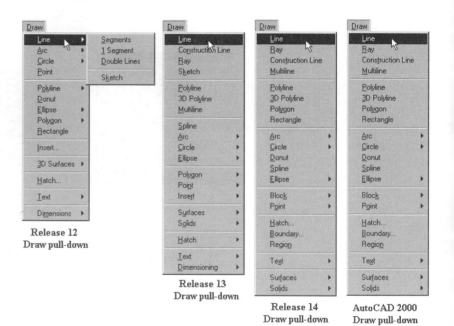

Fig. 1.7 The **Draw** menus

Command line prompt sequences

Figure 1.8 shows the appearance of the command line (Release 12) and command window (other releases) when the tool **Polyline** (pline) is called (it doesn't matter whether it is called by *clicking* on the **Polyline** tool icon in the **Draw** toolbox/toolbar or on the name in a **Draw** menu).

```
From point:
Current line-width is 0.00
Arc/Close/Halfwidth/Length/Undo/Width/<Endpoint of line>
```

Release 12 command line

```
Command: _pline
From point:
Current line-width is 0.0000
Arc/Close/Halfwidth/Length/Undo/Width/<Endpoint of line>
```

Release 13 command window

```
Command: _pline
From point:
Current line-width is 0
Arc/Close/Halfwidth/Length/Undo/Width/<Endpoint of line>:
```

Release 14 command window

Fig. 1.8 The command line (Release 12) and command windows (other releases) showing the **Polyline** prompt sequences

```
Command: _pline
Specify start point:
Current line-width is 0
Specify next point or [Arc/Close/Halfwidth/Length/Undo/Width]:
```

AutoCAD 2000 command window

The command line always shows a series of 'prompts', which are called by *entering* the capital letter of the prompt name. AutoCAD 2000 introduced a number of changes to the prompt line sequences of many tools, but the required responses are very similar. For example, when calling **Polyline** the following responses need to be made to make particular use of the methods involved:

Arc: *Enter* an **a** and another sequence of prompts appear.
Close: *Enter* a **c** and an open pline will close.
Length: *Enter* an **l** followed by a number and a line of that length will be drawn in the direction in which the cursor has been *dragged*.
Undo: *Enter* a **u** and the last action in the sequence is undone.
Width: *Enter* a **w** followed by a number and all parts of the pline are drawn to that width.

Note

1. Throughout this book the command line tool prompts sequences are shown in an abbreviated form with appropriate responses shown by the prompt capital letter, sometimes followed by the full prompt name in brackets:

For **Window** which is a common prompt: w (Window).
For **Center**, another fairly common prompt: c (Center).

2. In order to avoid confusion where the prompt sequences are slightly different between releases, long prompt sequence lines are often replaced by **'prompt sequence'**. For example, the responses to the **Polyline** prompt sequences illustrated in Fig. 1.7 would be shown as:

Command:_pline
From point: *enter* a coordinate figure *right-click*
Current line width is 0
prompt sequence: *enter* a (Arc) *right-click*
<Endpoint of arc>: *enter* s (Second point) *right-click*
Second point: *enter* a coordinate figure *right-click*
End point: *enter* a coordinate figure *right-click*
prompt sequence: *enter* l (Line) *right-click*

Abbreviations for tool names

Each release of AutoCAD uses a file for specifying abbreviations for tool names. This file **acad.pgp** (AutoCAD) or **aclt.pgp** (AutoCAD LT)) is kept in the **support** directory of the AutoCAD file structure. Therefore, in Release 12 the file is saved as **c:\acadwin\support\ acad.pgp**, and in AutoCAD 2000 it is saved as **c:\Program Files\ acad2000\support\acad**.

The **acad.pgp** file varies between releases; those of Releases 12 and 13 are not as complete as those of Release 14 and AutoCAD 2000. Abbreviations are entered into the file in the same way, no matter which release is in use:

L,   *LINE

If an abbreviation for a tool name is used in this book and does not result in the tool prompt sequences appearing in the command line, it is likely the abbreviation is not in your **acad.pgp** file. It is an easy matter to add an abbreviation to the file: open the file in the Notepad and add the abbreviation to those already listed using normal word processing methods. Figure 1.9 shows part of the **acad.pgp** file for Release 12 in its original form – that is without any operator additions.

Notes on loading AutoCAD for use

1. When AutoCAD Release 12 or 13 is launched, the AutoCAD window will be configured according to the default settings of the software.

```
; acad.pgp - External Command and Command Alias definitions

; External Command format:
;    <Command name>,[<DOS request>],<Memory reserve>,[*]<Prompt>,<Return code>

; Examples of External Commands for DOS

CATALOG,DIR /W,0,File specification: ,0
DEL,DEL,      0,File to delete: ,4
DIR,DIR,      0,File specification: ,0
EDIT,EDLIN,   0,File to edit: ,4
SH,,          0,*OS Command: ,4
SHELL,,       0,*OS Command: ,4
TYPE,TYPE,    0,File to list: ,0

; Command alias format:
;    <Alias>,*<Full command name>

; Sample aliases for AutoCAD Commands
; These examples reflect the most frequently used commands.
; Each alias uses a small amount of memory, so don't go
; overboard on systems with tight memory.

A,      *ARC
C,      *CIRCLE
CP,     *COPY
DV,     *DVIEW
E,      *ERASE
L,      *LINE
LA,     *LAYER
M,      *MOVE
MS,     *MSPACE
P,      *PAN
PS,     *PSPACE
PL,     *PLINE
```

Fig. 1.9 Part of the Release 12 **acad.pgp** file

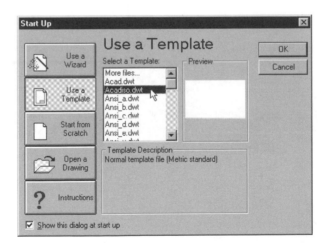

Fig. 1.10 **Use a Template** dialog box (Release 14)

2. When AutoCAD Release 14 or 2000 is launched the **Use a Template** dialog box appears. You can make up your own templates that can be added to the templates listed in the **Use a Template** dialog box (see Figures 1.10 and 1.11).

Fig. 1.11 **Use a Template**
dialog box (AutoCAD 2000)

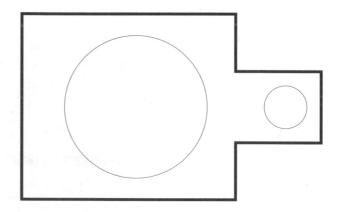

Fig. 1.12 A simple AutoCAD
drawing

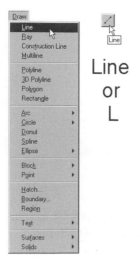

Fig. 1.13 Methods of calling
the **Line** tool

Example of a simple drawing

Figure 1.12 shows a simple drawing which can be constructed in
any of the AutoCAD releases using the methods described in this
book. When a new tool is introduced, all four methods of calling
the tool will be shown in illustrations and in text. It must be
remembered that the menus will vary somewhat between releases,
but that the tool being used will be available from the menu as
shown in the illustration.

This example involves the tools **Line**, **Circle** and **Polyline Edit**
(pedit). The **Polyline Edit** tool icon is found in the **Special Edit**
(Release 13) or **Modify II** (Release 14 and AutoCAD 2000) toolbar.

Call the **Line** tool (Fig. 1.13) – *click* on its tool icon in the **Draw**
toolbar, *click* on its name in the **Draw** menu, or *enter* **line** or **l** at
the command line:

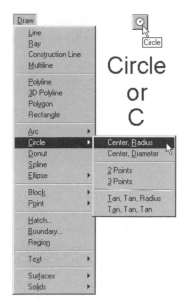

Fig. 1.14 Methods of calling the **Circle** tool

Fig. 1.15 Methods of calling the **Polyline Edit** tool

Command:_line From point: *enter* 120,230 *right-click*
To point: *enter* 270,230 *right-click*
To point: *enter* 270,190 *right-click*
To point: *enter* 330,190 *right-click*
To point: *enter* 330,140 *right-click*
To point: *enter* 270,140 *right-click*
To point: *enter* 270,100 *right-click*
To point: *enter* 120,100 *right-click*
To point: *enter* c (Close) *right-click*
Command:

Call the **Circle** tool (Fig. 1.14) – *click* on its tool icon in the **Draw** toolbar, *click* on its name in the **Draw** menu, or *enter* **line** or l at the command line:

Command:_circle
<Center point>: *enter* 305,165 *right-click*
<Radius>: *enter* 15 *right-click*
Command: *right-click*
Command:_circle
<Center point>: *enter* 205,170 *right-click*
<Radius>: *enter* 50 *right-click*
Command:

Call the **Polyline Edit** tool (Fig. 1.15) – *click* on its tool icon in the **Special Edit** toolbar (Release 13) or the **Modify II** toolbar (Release 14 and AutoCAD 2000), *click* on its name in the **Modify** menu, or *enter* **pedit** or **pe** at the command line:

Command:_pedit Select polyline *pick* one of the lines
Object selected is not a polyline
Do you want to turn it into one?<Y>: *right-click*
prompt sequence: *enter* j (Join) *right-click*
Select objects: *enter* w (Window)
First corner: *pick* **Other corner:** *pick* **11 found**
Select objects: *right-click*
7 segments added to polyline
prompt sequence: *enter* w (Width) *right-click*
Enter new width for all segments: *enter* 2 *right-click*
prompts sequence: *right-click*
Command:

The AutoCAD coordinate system

No matter which release of AutoCAD you are using, the working area of the screen is divided into an invisible grid of points known as coordinate units. The number of units horizontally and vertically is determined using the **Limits** tool. To set up the working area as a horizontal (landscape) A3 sheet of paper:

Command: *enter* limits *right-click*
ON/OFF <Lower left corner>: <0,0>: *right-click*
Upper right corner <12,9>: *enter* 420,297 *right-click*
Command: zoom
prompt sequence: *enter* a (for All) *right-click*
Command:

Why 420,297? Because an A3 sheet of paper is 420 mm by 297 mm. This means that when working in the AutoCAD drawing area as set up above, each coordinate unit represents 1 millimetre on an A3 drawing. This is the typical working area used throughout the examples and exercises in this book.

When the **Limits** command is used as above, points on the screen can be *picked* or *entered* as indicated in Fig. 1.16. Such points are referred to in terms of *x* and *y*, the *x* units being the number of coordinate units horizontally, the *y* the number of units vertically. Usually (but not always) the bottom left-hand corner is the coordinate position in which *x,y* = 0,0. Other coordinate positions are the unit lengths horizontally and vertically from the 'origin' where *x,y* = 0,0. Thus the point *x,y* = 100,150 is 100 units to the right of and 150 units above *x,y* = 0,0.

Fig. 1.16 Coordinate points in an AutoCAD 2000 window set to A3 unit sizes

Points to the left and/or below the origin are shown as negative numbers, thus the point x,y = -100,-150 is 100 units to the left of and 150 units below the origin.

The AutoCAD cursor hairs

Two crossing lines are usually seen when an AutoCAD drawing is opened; these move as the mouse is moved. To *pick* a point on screen, move the mouse and *left-click* when the intersection of the cursor hairs is at the desired position.

Note

The coordinate units position (in numbers) of the intersecting point of the cursor hairs shows either at the top (Release 12) or the bottom left (other releases) of the AutoCAD window. As the mouse is moved, the coordinate numbers constantly change to show the position of the intersection of the cursor hairs as numeric coordinates. Figure 1.17 shows the cursor hairs and the coordinates in the status bar at the bottom of a Release 13 window.

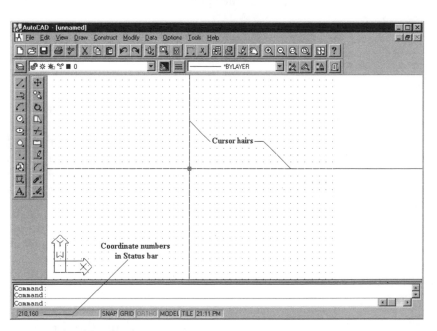

Fig. 1.17 Cursor hairs and coordinate figures in a Release 13 window

Grid and Snap

Call **Grid** as follows:

Command: *enter* grid *right-click*
Grid spacing (X) or ON/OFF/Snap/Aspect <1>: *enter* 10 *right-click*
Command:

The best method of setting the grid points on or off is to press the **F7** key, which 'toggles' the grid on and off. When the grid is 'on' the drawing area is covered by a grid of dots (the distances between the dots are set by calling the **Grid** command as above).

Call **Snap** as follows:

Command: *enter* snap *right-click*
Snap spacing or ON/OFF/Aspect/Rotate/Style <1>: *enter* 5 *right-click*
Command:

The best method of setting the snap function on or off is to press the **F9** key, which toggles the function on or off. When snap is on, as the cursor hairs are moved by *dragging* the mouse, the intersection point of the cursors jumps between the snap points. In the example above the intersection point would jump between snap points set 5 units apart.

Using grid points can help the operator to assess coordinate points when constructing outlines. The snap function allows accurate positioning of points on screen.

The mouse as a digitiser

There are a number of different devices which can be used with AutoCAD for *selecting* commands, and for *picking* points or features on screen. These devices are known as 'digitisers'. In this book it is assumed that a two-button mouse will be used. The left mouse button is referred to as the 'pick' button and the right mouse button is called the 'return' button. Note that pressing the return button of a mouse *usually* has the same result as pressing the **Return** or **Enter** key of the computer keyboard and vice versa – but not always.

Note

When working in Release 12, if the wrong command has been called, pressing the **Ctrl** key and the **C** key at the same time cancels the command and the command line to revert to **Command:**. In later versions pressing the **Esc** key has the same result.

Ten-point summary

1. The methods employed throughout this book are common to all four releases of AutoCAD which will operate under Windows 95/98/NT.

2. No matter which release is in use, the AutoCAD can be launched by *double-clicking* the appropriate application icon on the Windows desktop.

3. Usually tools (which some refer to as commands) can be called for use by one of four methods:

With a *click* on the tool's icon in a toolbar.
With a *click* on the tool's name in a menu.
By *entering* the name of the tool in full at the command line.
By *entering* an abbreviation of the tool name at the command line.

Operators will choose their own methods of working, which is often a mixture of the four methods.

4. There are small differences in the prompt sequences seen at the command line between different releases. Because of these differences, long command line prompt sequences will at times be shown as **prompt sequence:**, but an explanation of the available prompts as they would generally be used will also be included.

5. The AutoCAD coordinate units system is important for the production of accurate drawings and examples of using the system will be seen throughout this book.

6. Early examples in this book will be 2D drawings involving two-figure coordinates in the form *x,y*. Later, when dealing with 3D drawing, three-figure coordinates will be used in the form *x,y,z*.

7. Most of the drawings in this book have been constructed in drawing areas set to 420 by 297 (A3 metric sizes in millimetres).

8. On this A3 sheet **Grid** and **Snap** are usually set on. This helps the accuracy of most constructional work in AutoCAD. In this book **Grid** is normally set to 10 and **Snap** to 5.

9. It is important to remember that **Grid** can be toggled with the **F7** key and **Snap** with the **F9** key. It helps considerably to be able to toggle these two features on and off quickly when required.

10. Also remember that in Release 12 pressing **Ctrl+C**, and in later releases pressing the **Esc** key, cancels any tool operation functioning at the time. Later releases can be configured to use **Ctrl+C** if so desired, but it is usually easier to use the **Esc** key.

Saving your drawings

It is advisable to save drawings to disk not only when the drawing has been completed, but also at intervals during the period spent constructing them. Saving at regular intervals of time (say about every 15 minutes) will prevent any significant loss of work if the computer crashes for any reason, or if there is a power cut.

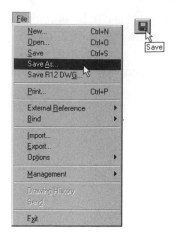

Fig. 1.18 Calling **Save As** or **Save**

Fig. 1.19 The **Save Drawing As** dialog box (Release 14)

To save a drawing to file *select* **Save As** from the **File** menu or *click* on the **Save** icon at the top of the AutoCAD window (Fig. 1.18). When the **Save Drawing As** dialog box appears *enter* a suitable filename in the box and *click* on the **Save** button in the dialog box (Fig. 1.19). Figure 1.19 shows the **Save Drawing As** dialog box of Release 14.

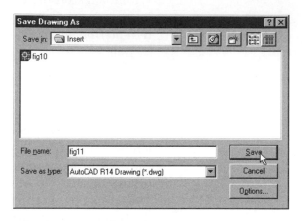

Note

When working through the worked examples and exercises in this book, it is advisable to save each drawing as it is constructed. And unless you own the computer it is advisable to save them to a floppy disk and not to the computer's hard disk.

CHAPTER 2

Simple constructions

Setting up an A3 drawing window

The **Units** and **Limits** settings of an A3 landscape AutoCAD drawing window can be set up as follows. Further details about setting
up AutoCAD will be given in later chapters.

Setting limits

At the command line:

Command: *enter* limits *right-click*
ON/OFF/<Lower left corner> <0,0>: *right-click*
Upper right corner <12,9>: *enter* 420,297 *right-click*
Command: *enter* z (Zoom) *right-click*
prompts sequence: *enter* a (All) *right-click*
Command:

Setting units

Throughout the book we are only concerned with whole units
(with no figures after the decimal point). Units can be set from a
dialog box as shown in Fig. 2.1, but they can also be set by:

Command: *enter* units *right-click*

The **AutoCAD Text Window** appears in which the required units
parameters can be set manually (Fig. 2.2).

Saving your window set-up

If working with Releases 12 or 13 *select* **Save As . . .** from the **File**
menu. In the **Save Drawing As** dialog box save the drawing using
the filename **support\acad.dwg**. When using Release 14 and
AutoCAD 2000, save your drawing as a template (Fig. 2.3): *select*
Drawing template file (*.dwt) from the **File of type** list and save
using a suitable filename – in this example (Fig. 2.3) I have used

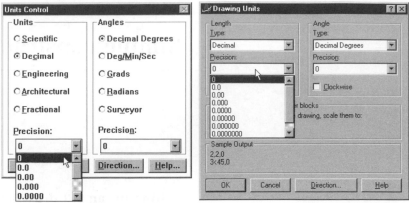

Fig. 2.1 Setting units from a
dialog box

Release 12   AutoCAD 2000

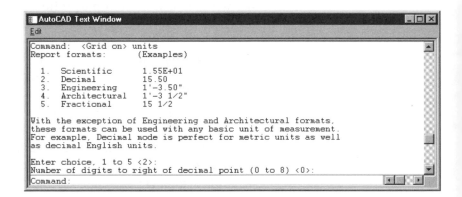

Fig. 2.2 Setting units from
the command line

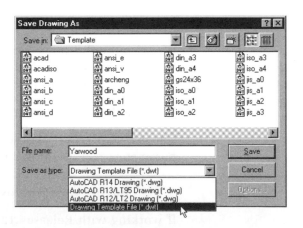

Fig. 2.3 The **Save Drawing
As** dialog box when saving a
drawing template

my own name (**Yarwood**). The next time I open AutoCAD I can
select the template **Yarwood.dwt** to open a drawing set up as
before. Later in this book additions and changes will be made to
either the **acad.dwg** or the **Yarwood.dwt** template.

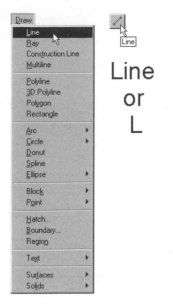

Fig. 2.4 Calling the **Line** tool

Constructions using the Line tool

Line: example 1 (Fig. 2.5)

Call the **Line** tool – *click* on the **Line** tool icon in the **Draw** toolbar (Release 12 toolbox), *click* on **Line** in the **Draw** menu, or *enter* **line** or **l** at the command line (Fig. 2.4):

Command:_line From point: *enter* 80,230 *right-click*
To point: *enter* 290,230 *right-click*
To point: *enter* 290,110 *right-click*
To point: *enter* 230,110 *right-click*
To point: *enter* 230,140 *right-click*
To point: *enter* 140,140 *right-click*
To point: *enter* 140,110 *right-click*
To point: *enter* 80,110 *right-click*
To point: *enter* c (Close) *right-click*
Command:

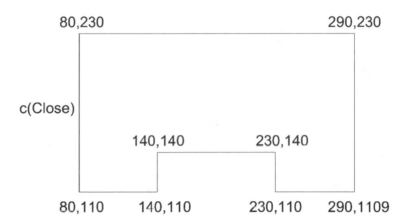

Fig. 2.5 Example 1

Line: example 2 (Fig. 2.6)

Command:_line From point: *enter* 80,220 *right-click*
To point: *enter* 22,220 *right-click*
To point: *enter* 220,180 *right-click*
To point: *enter* 370,180 *right-click*
To point: *enter* 370,140 *right-click*
To point: *enter* 220,140 *right-click*
To point: *enter* 220,100 *right-click*
To point: *enter* 80,100 *right-click*
To point: *enter* 80,130 *right-click*
To point: *enter* 100,150 *right-click*
To point: *enter* 100,170 *right-click*

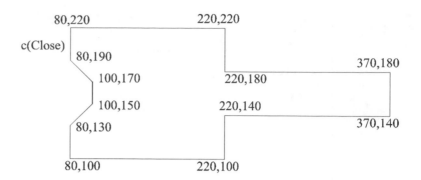

Fig. 2.6 Example 2

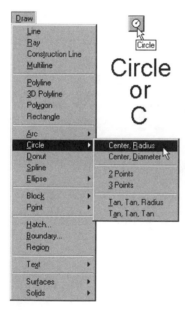

Fig. 2.7 Calling the **Circle** tool

To point: *enter* 80,190 *right-click*
To point: *enter* c (Close) *right-click*
Command:

Constructions using the Circle tool

Each circle formed with the aid of this tool is an object in its own right. The prompts associated with the tool are:

2P: Construct a circle given two points on its circumference.
3P: Construct a circle given three points on its circumference.
TTR (Tangent/Tangent/Radius): Form a circle touching two other circles or a circle and another object (e.g. a line).
Center point: *Enter* or *pick* the centre of the required circle.
Diameter: *Enter* or *pick* the required diameter of the circle.
Radius: *Enter* or *pick* the required radius of the circle.

Circle (Fig. 2.8)

Call the **Circle** tool – *click* on the **Circle** tool icon in the **Draw** toolbar (Release 12 toobox), *click* on **Circle** in the **Draw** menu, or *enter* **circle** or **c** at the command line (Fig. 2.7). Note that a sub-menu appears on the **Draw** menu when **Circle** is *selected*.

This example consists of four parts as shown by the numbers against the parts of Fig. 2.8.

Circle (drawing 1)

Command:_circle
3P/2P/TTR/<Center point>: *enter* 80,110 *right-click*
Diameter/<Radius>: *enter* 60 *right-click*
Command:

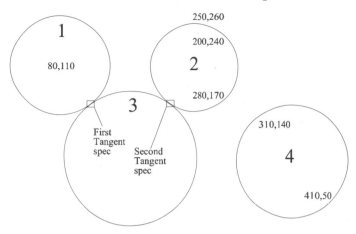

Fig. 2.8 **Circle** example

Circle (drawing 2)

Command:_circle
3P/2P/TTR/<Center point>: *enter* 3p
First point: *enter* 200,240 *right-click*
Second point: *enter* 250,260 *right-click*
Third point: *enter* 280,170 *right-click*
Command:

Circle (drawing 3)

Command:_circle
3P/2P/TTR/<Center point>: *enter* ttr *right-click*
Enter Tangent spec: *pick* a point on circle 1
Enter second Tangent spec: *pick* a point on circle 2
Radius: *enter* 80 *right-click*
Command:

Circle (drawing 4)

Command:_circle
3P/2P/TTR/<Center point>: *enter* 2p *right-click*
First point on diameter: *enter* 310,140 *right-click*
Second point on diameter: *enter* 410,50 *right-click*
Command:

Constructions using the Arc tool

Call the **Arc** tool – *click* on the **Arc** tool icon in the **Draw** toolbar (Release 12 toolbox), *click* on **Arc** in the **Draw** menu, or *enter* **arc** or **a** at the command line (Fig. 2.9). Note a sub-menu appears on the **Draw** menu when **Arc** is *selected*.

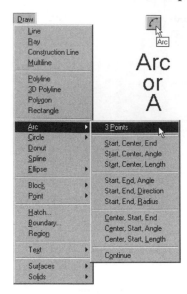

Fig. 2.9 Calling the **Arc** tool

Arc (Fig. 2.10)

This example consists of four parts as shown by the numbers against the parts of Fig. 2.10.

Arc (drawing 1)

Command:_arc
Center/<Start point>: *enter* 25,230 *right-click*
Center/End/Second point: *enter* 80,275 *right-click*
End point: *enter* 165,230 *right-click*
Command:

Arc (drawing 2)

Command:_arc
Center/<Start point>: *enter* c *right-click*
Center: *enter* 285,215 *right-click*
Start point: *enter* 365,235 *right-click*
Angle/Length of chord/<End point>: *enter* 215,255 *right-click*
Command:

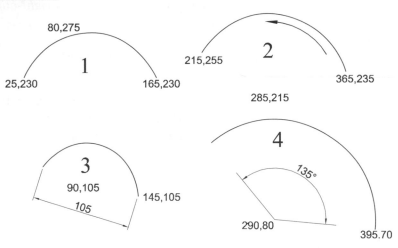

Fig. 2.10 **Arc** example

Note

The default rotation of an arc being drawn is anticlockwise (counterclockwise): the arrow direction is shown in drawing 2.

Arc (drawing 3)

Command:_arc
Center/<Start point>: *enter* c *right-click*
Center: *enter* 90,105 *right-click*
Start point: *enter* 145,105 *right-click*

Angle/Length of chord/<End point>: *enter* l (Length) *right-click*
Length of chord: *enter* 105 *right-click*
Command:

Arc (drawing 4)

Command:_arc
Center/<Start point>: *enter* c *right-click*
Center: *enter* 290,80 *right-click*
Start point: *enter* 395,70 *right-click*
Angle/Length of chord/<End point>: *enter* a (Angle) *right-click*
Included angle: *enter* 135 *right-click*
Command:

Tool name abbreviations

The abbreviations for the most frequently used **Draw** tools in the four AutoCAD releases are as follows:

Line	**l**
Construction line	**xl** (release 13 onwards)
Polyline (pline)	**pl**
Polygon	**pol**
Rectangle	**rec** (release 13 onwards)
Arc	**a**
Circle	**c**
Ellipse	**el**
Dtext	**dt**

Fig. 2.11 Calling the **Undo** and **Redo** tools

Note

When using abbreviations in AutoCAD Release 12 for Windows it may be necessary to check the **acad.pgp** file to see if the abbreviation has been included.

The Undo and Redo tools

The abbreviation **u** for **Undo** can be used at any time during a construction sequence. For example, if a circle has been drawn *entering* **u** causes the circle just drawn to disappear from the screen. If the tool is *entered* over and over again, you will eventually undo everything that has been constructed on screen. When this happens **Everything has been undone** appears at the command line.

The command **Redo** will only bring back the last object to be undone. Repeated use of **Redo** has no effect.

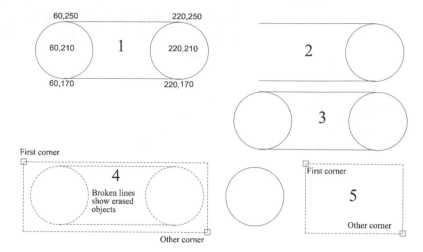

Fig. 2.12 **Undo** and **Erase** example

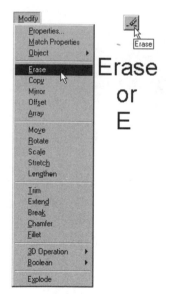

Fig. 2.13 Calling the **Erase** tool

The Erase tool

By far the easiest method of calling **Erase** in any of the AutoCAD releases is to *enter* **e** at the command line. The tool can also be called from the **Modify** menu or by *clicking* the **Erase** icon in the **Modify** toolbar (see Fig. 2.13).

Using the tools **Circle** and **Line** construct Fig. 2.12, drawing 1.

Erase and Undo (drawings 2 and 3)

Command: *enter* e *right-click*
Select objects: *pick* the left-hand circle – it is removed from the screen (drawing **2**)
Command: *enter* u (Undo) *right-click* and the circle reappears (drawing **3**)
ERASE GROUP
Command:

Erase (drawing 4)

Command: *enter* erase *right-click*
Select objects: *enter* w (for Window) *right-click*
First corner: *pick* point above the left-hand corner of the outline
Other corner: *pick* point below the right-hand corner of the outline
4 found
Select objects: *right-click* or *Return* and all objects disappear
Command: *enter* u (Undo) *right-click* and the outline reappears
ERASE GROUP
Command:

Note

All objects within the window are erased.

Erase (drawing 5)

Command: *enter* erase *right-click*
Select objects: *enter* c (for Crossing window) *right-click*
First corner: *pick* point above the left hand corner of the outline
Other corner: *pick* point below the right hand corner of the outline
3 found
Select objects: *right-click* or *Return* and the three objects disappear
Command:

Note

All objects which are crossed by the lines of the crossing window
are erased.

The relative coordinate entry method

The worked examples shown so far have all been constructed
using what is known as the 'absolute' coordinate entry method. As
each prompt at the command line appears coordinate points are
entered (as *x,y*) for each point in the construction. In the 'relative'
coordinate entry method, the unit distance or angle *between* points
in a construction is *entered* at the prompts. The method involves
entering @ before the *x,y* coordinate points and, in the case of
angles, *entering* < before the angle size (in degrees).

Remember that *x* units are horizontal and *y* units are vertical,
and note that the *x,y* coordinates used in the relative coordinate
entry method are in unit lengths between points in an outline:

x unit distances to the *right* of the last point are positive.
x unit distances to the *left* of the last point are negative.
y unit distances *above* the last point are positive.
y unit distances *below* the last point are negative.

By default, angles are measured in degrees in an anticlockwise
direction from 0° to the right of the origin. Figure 2.14 shows angles
at 30° intervals measured in this manner.

Construction involving relative coordinate entry

Note

So far the entries at the command line have been shown in the form:

Command: *enter* e (Erase) *right-click*

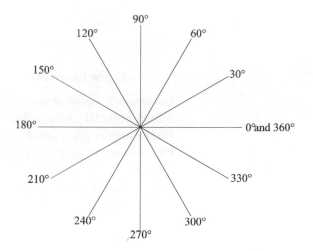

Fig. 2.14 Measuring angles
anticlockwise

From now on the presentation will be simplified to:

Command: e (Erase)

Relative coordinates: example 1 (Fig. 2.15)

Command:_line
From point: 70,230 (A)
To point: @200,0 (gives B)
To point: @0,-50 (gives C)
To point: @-20,0 (gives D)
To point: @0,-40 (gives E)
To point: @20,0 (gives F)
To point: @0,-50 (gives G)
To point: @-200,0 (gives H)
To point: @0,50 (gives J)
To point: @20,0 (gives K)
To point: @0,40 (gives L)

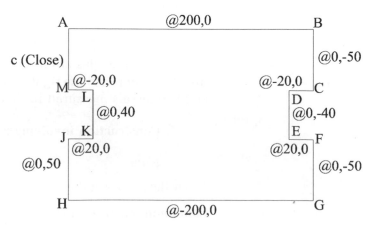

Fig. 2.15 Example 1

To point: @-20,0 (gives M)
To point: c (Close) (back to A)
Command:

Relative coordinates: example 2 (Fig. 2.16)

Command:_line
From point: 110,230 (A)
To point: @170,0 (B)
To point: @60<330 (C)
To point: @0,-8 (D)
To point: @60,<210 (E)
To point: @0,-8 (F)
To point: @60<330 (H)
To point: @0,-8 (J)
To point: @60<210 (K)

And so on until *entering* **c** (for Close) at point T completes the outline.

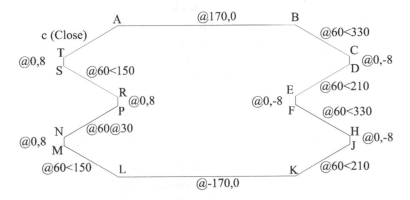

Fig. 2.16 Example 2

Relative coordinates: example 3 (Fig. 2.17, drawing 1)

Command:_arc
Center/<Start point>: 10,225
Center/End/<Second point>: @100,50
End point: @100,-50
Command:

Relative coordinates: example 4 (Fig. 2.17, drawing 2)

Command:_line
From point: 35,160
To point: @200,0
To point: *right-click*
Command:_arc

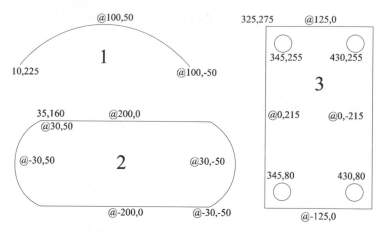

Fig. 2.17 Examples 3–5

Center/<Start point>: 235,160
Center/End/<Second point>: @30,-50
End point: @-30,-50
Command:_line
From point: 235,60
To point: @-200,0
To point: *right-click*
Command: *right-click*
ARCCenter/<Start point>: 35,60
Center/End/<Second point>: @-30,50
End point: @30,50
Command:

Relative coordinates: example 5 (Fig. 2.17, drawing 3)

Command:_line
From point: 325,275
To point: @125,0

And continue to complete the rectangle. Then:

Command:circle
3P/2P/TTR/<Center point>: 345,255
Diameter/<Radius>: 10
Command:

Repeat the circle command to add the other three circles. Their centre point coordinate positions are given below each circle in Fig. 2.17, drawing 3.

Object snaps (osnaps)

Osnaps are a valuable aid to the production of accurate drawings. The use of osnaps allows the exact positioning of objects relative to objects already on screen. With their aid, points of objects can

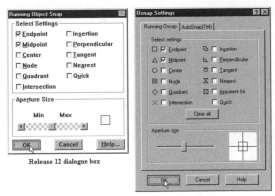

Fig. 2.18 Osnap dialog boxes
(Release 12, Release 14 and
AutoCAD 2000)

AutoCAD 2000 dialogue box

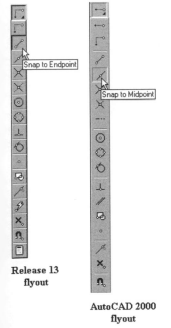

Release 13
flyout

AutoCAD 2000
flyout

Fig. 2.19 Osnap flyouts
(Release 13 and AutoCAD
2000)

be added to a construction to connect exactly: to the endpoint or
midpoint of another object; perpendicular to another object; to the
intersection of two objects; to the centre, quadrant point or tangent
to a circle or arc; to the nearest point on another object.

From Release 12 to AutoCAD 2000 and in LT, methods of calling osnaps have improved. In all releases they can be set from
dialog boxes, examples of which are shown in Fig. 2.18. In Release
13 to AutoCAD 2000 they can also be called from flyouts from the
Standard toolbar (see Fig. 2.19). In all releases an abbreviation for
the appropriate osnap can be *entered* at the command line as shown
in the following examples. It is this method which is used throughout this book. The abbreviations are:

Endpoint	**end**
Midpoint	**mid**
Intersection	**int**
Perpendicular	**perp**
Centre	**cen**
Quadrant	**qua**
Tangent	**tan**
Nearest	**nea**

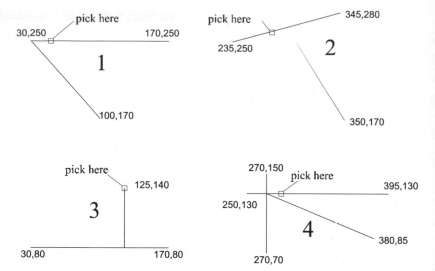

Fig. 2.20 Examples 1–4

Osnaps: example 1 (Fig. 2.20, drawing 1)

Draw the line from 30,250 to 170,250. Then:

Command:_line
From point: 100,170
To point: end
of *pick* near the end of the line on screen
To point: *right-click*
Command:

Osnaps: example 2 (Fig. 2.20, drawing 2)

Draw a line from 235,150 to 345,280. Then:

Command:_line
From point: 350,170
To point: mid
of *pick* near the middle point of the line on screen
To point: *right-click*
Command:

Osnaps: example 3 (Fig. 2.20, drawing 3)

Draw a line from 30,80 to 170,80. Then:

Command:_line
From point: 125,140
To point: perp
of *pick* on the line
To point: *right-click*
Command:

Osnaps: example 4 (Fig. 2.20, drawing 4)

Draw a line from 250,130 to 395,130 and a second line from 270,150 to 270,70.

Command:_line
From point: 380,85
To point: int
of *pick* near the point where the two lines cross
To point: *right-click*
Command:

Osnaps: example 5 (Fig. 2.21, drawing 5)

Draw a circle of centre 50,235 and of radius 50. Draw a second circle of centre 50,80 and radius 50.

Command:_line
From point: qua
of *pick* near the point of the upper quadrant of the lower circle
To point: tan
of *pick* near the point tangency to the upper circle
To point: *right-click*
Command:

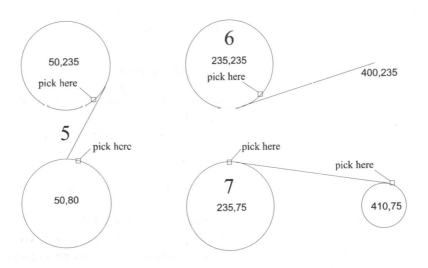

Fig. 2.21 Examples 5–7

Osnaps: example 6 (Fig. 2.21, drawing 6)

Draw a circle of centre 235,235 and of radius 50.

Command:_line
From point: 400,235

To point: tan
of *pick* near the tangency point of the circle
To point: *right-click*
Command:

Osnaps: example 7 (Fig. 2.21, drawing 7)

Draw a circle of centre 235,7 of radius 50. Draw a second circle of centre 410,75 of radius 25

Command:_line
From point: tan
of *pick* near the tangency point of the smaller circle
To point: tan
of *pick* near the tangency point of the larger circle
To point: *right-click*
Command:

Coordinates

As the cursor is moved, the position of the intersection of the cursor hairs shows up as *x,y* coordinates in the menubar (Release 12) or at the bottom left-hand corner of the command line window in later releases (see Fig. 2.22). Pressing **Ctrl+D** causes the coordinates to cycle between showing absolute numbers, showing relative numbers and showing no numbers.

Release 12 - top of window

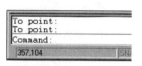

Other release - bottom of Command line window

Fig. 2.22 Coordinate display in Release 12 and other releases

Questions

1. Can you explain the meaning of coordinate units as used in AutoCAD?
2. What are the differences between drawing in AutoCAD using absolute coordinates and using relative coordinates?
3. When using the command **Circle**, when would you *enter* **c** at the command line and what does it mean?
4. When using the command **Circle**, for what purpose would you use the prompt **TTR**?
5. When using the command **Arc** a number of prompts are available allowing arcs to be constructed in various of ways. Can you write down those prompts?
6. If, while *entering* coordinates at the command line, you *enter* an incorrect coordinate, how can you cancel the error?
7. What is the effect of using the command **Redo**?
8. If you wish to erase several objects from a drawing on screen what methods can be used?

9. When constructing an arc, in which direction would the arc be formed?
10. In which direction relative to an angle vertex is the angle 0°?

Exercises

Figures 2.23–2.32 are outlines which can be constructed using the methods given in this chapter. Construct each of the outlines in turn. (Do not attempt to add dimensions to any of your drawings.)

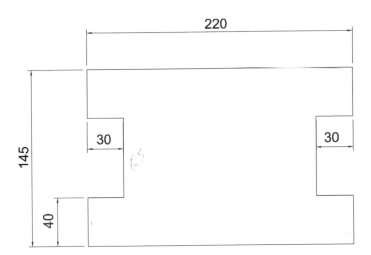

Fig. 2.23 Exercise 1

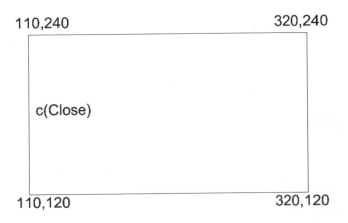

Fig. 2.24 Exercise 2

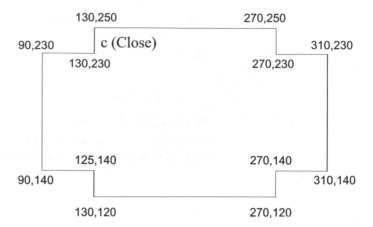

Fig. 2.25 Exercise 3

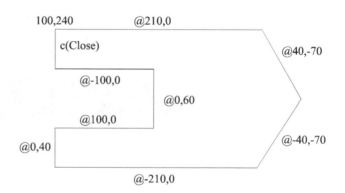

Fig. 2.26 Exercise 4

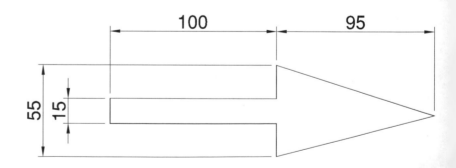

Fig. 2.27 Exercise 5

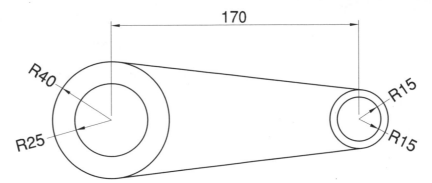

Fig. 2.28 Exercise 6

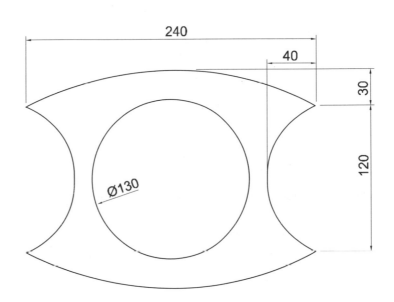

Fig. 2.29 Exercise 7

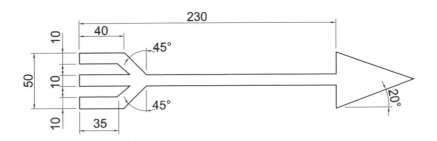

Fig. 2.30 Exercise 8

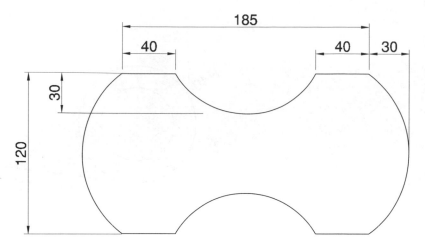

Fig. 2.31 Exercise 9

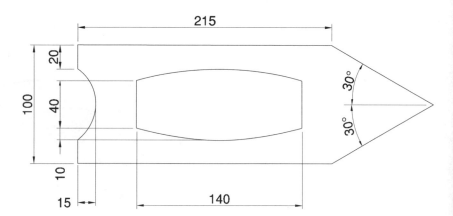

Fig. 2.32 Exercise 10

CHAPTER 3

The Polyline tool

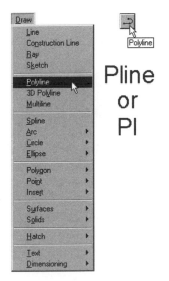

Fig. 3.1 Calling the **Polyline** (**Pline**) tool

Introduction

When an outline is constructed with the aid of the command line, each part of the outline is a separate object. When an outline is constructed with the aid of the command **Polyline**, the whole outline is a single object.

Lines constructed with the command **Line** are always simply straight lines of width 0. Polylines however can be of varying widths or, if desired, can be formed into arcs. Even if different polyline widths and arcs are included in a single polyline outline, the outline is a single object.

To call the **Polyline** tool, *click* on its tool icon in the **Draw** toolbar (Release 12 toolbox), *click* on **Polyline** in the **Modify** menu, or *enter* **pline** or **pl** at the command line (Fig. 3.1). Although the prompt sequences from the various releases of AutoCAD vary slightly, in general when the **Polyline** tool is called the command line shows:

Command:_pline
From point: *pick* a point
Current line width is 0
Arc/Close/Halfwidth/Length/Undo/Width/<Endpoint of line>:

Note

Remember: Long lines of prompts such as the last one in the sequence above may be shown in this book in the form '**prompt sequence:**'.

Polyline outlines of varying widths

Polyline: example 1 (Fig. 3.2)

Command:_pline
From point: *pick* a point

Current line width is 0
prompt sequence: w (Width)
Starting width <0>: 1
Ending width <1>: *right-click*
prompt sequence: @250,0
prompt sequence: @0,-150
prompt sequence: @-250,0
prompt sequence: c (Close)
Command:

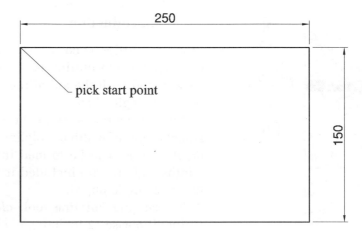

Fig. 3.2 Example 1

Polyline: example 2 (Fig. 3.3)

Command:_pline
From point: *pick* a point
Current line width is 1
prompt sequence: w (Width)
Starting width <1>: 3
Ending width <3>: *right-click*
prompt sequence: @200,0
prompt sequence: w (Width)
Starting width <0>: 20
Ending width <20>: 0
prompt sequence: @50,0
prompt sequence: *right-click*
Command:

Fig. 3.3 Example 2

Polyline: example 3 (Fig. 3.4)

Command:_pline
From point: 70,230
Current line width is 0
prompt sequence: w (Width)
Starting width <0>: 2
Ending width <2>: *right-click*
prompt sequence: @220,0
prompt sequence: a (Arc)
prompt sequence: s (Second pt)
Second point: 320,170
Endpoint: 290,110
prompt sequence: l (Line)
prompt sequence: @-200,0
prompt sequence: a (Arc)
prompt sequence: s (Second pt)
Second point: 40,170
Endpoint: 70,230
prompt sequence: cl (CLose)
Command:

70,230

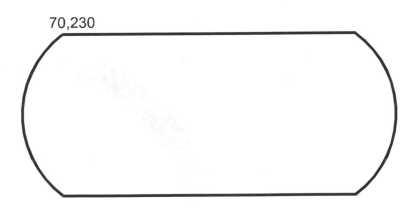

Fig. 3.4 Example 3

Note

The prompt sequence when the response is **a** (for **Arc**) is:

Angle/CEntre/CLose/Direction/Halfwidth/Line/Radius/Second pt/
Undo/Width/<Endpoint of arc>:

Polyline: example 4 (Fig. 3.5)

Command:_circle
3P/2P/TTR/<Center point>: 220,140
Diameter/<Radius>: 130

Command: pline
From point: qua **of** *pick* near left hand quadrant of circle
Current line width is 0
Endpoint: 290,110
prompt sequence: l (Line)
prompt sequence: @-200,0
prompt sequence: a (Arc)
prompt sequence: s (Second pt)
Second point: 40,170
Endpoint: 70,230 cl (CLose)
Command:

Polyline: example 4 (Fig. 3.5)

Command:_circle
3P/2P/TTR/<Center point>: 220,140
Diameter/<Radius>: 130
Command: pline
From point: qua **of** *pick* near left hand quadrant of circle
Current line width is 0
prompt sequence: w (Width)
Starting width <0>: 20

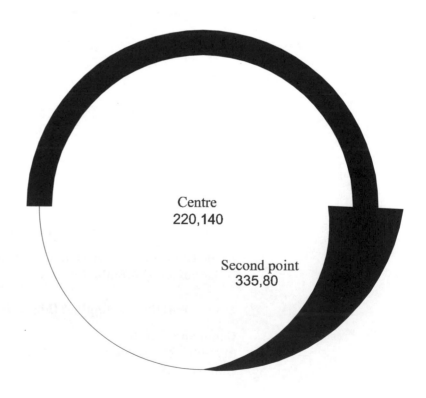

Fig. 3.5 Example 4

Ending width <20>: 20
prompt sequence: a (Arc)
prompt sequence: s (Second pt) w (Width)
Starting width <0>: 20
Ending width <20>: 20
prompt sequence: a (Arc)
prompt sequence: s (Second pt)
Second point: qua **of** *pick* near upper quadrant of circle
Endpoint: qua **of** *pick* near right hand quadrant of circle w (Width)
Starting width <20>: 60
Ending width <60>: 0
Second point: 335,80
prompt sequence: s (Second pt)
Endpoint: qua **of** *pick* near bottom quadrant of circle
<Endpoint of arc>: *right-click*
Command:

The circle can now be erased if desired.

Notes

The series of prompts associated with the command **Polyline** appear to be very complicated but you will find that this example can be completed very quickly once the methods of responding to the **Polyline** prompts have been mastered.

Drawing using the other prompts available in the **Polyline** series can now be attempted.

The direct entry method

Another method of obtaining accurately measured drawings is to use the 'direct entry' method (not available in Release 12):

1. *Drag* the 'rubber band' line from the last point *entered* towards the direction in which the next line or polyline of the outline is to be drawn.
2. *Enter* the length of next line or polyline at command line.

Polyline direct entry: example 1 (Fig. 3.6)

Command:_pline
From point: 60,240
Current line width is 0
prompt sequence: w (Width)
Starting width <0>: 0.7
Ending width <1>: *right-click*
prompt sequence: *drag* rubber band to right and *enter* 205

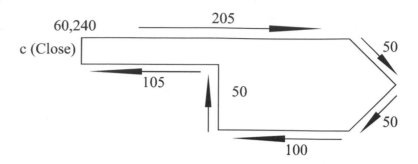

Fig. 3.6 Example 1

prompt sequence: press **F9** to toggle **Snap** off; press **Ctrl+D** to show coordinates at top or bottom of screen in relative units; *drag* rubber band until the coordinate angle is showing **<315** and *enter* 50

prompt sequence: *drag* rubber band until **<215** shows and *enter* 50

Continue in this manner to complete the outline as shown in Fig. 3.5.

Notes

1. Note the method of setting the way in which coordinate figures are shown either at top or bottom of the screen when **Ctrl+D** keys are pressed. The toggling is between no coordinate numbers showing to absolute entry numbers showing to relative numbers showing.
2. **Ctrl+D** to toggle coordinates showing can be carried out during constructions of outlines.
3. The direct method of construction can be alternated with either absolute coordinate entry or relative coordinate entry. Many constructions will be based upon a mixture of the three methods.

Polyline direct entry: example 2 (Fig. 3.7)

This example uses all three methods of construction: absolute, relative and direct.

Command:_pline
From point: 75,215
Current line width is 0
prompt sequence: w (Width)
Starting width <0>: 0.7
Ending width <1>: *right-click*
prompt sequence: *drag* rubber band to right and *enter* 60
prompt sequence: a (Arc)
prompt sequence: s (Second pt)

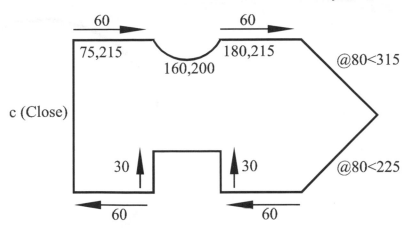

Fig. 3.7 Example 2

Second point: 160,200
Endpoint: 180,215
prompt sequence: l (Line)
prompt sequence: 60
prompt sequence: @80<315
prompt sequence: @80<225

Continue as shown in Fig. 3.7 to complete the outline.

Polyline: circle example (Fig. 3.8)

This example shows two methods for constructing circles using the **Polyline** command. The first method is:

Command:_pline
From point: 60,195
Current line width is 0
prompt sequence: w (Width)
Starting width: 3
Ending width <3>: *right-click*
prompt sequence: a (Arc)
prompt sequence: s (Second pt)
prompt sequence: 110,245
End point: 160,195
prompt sequence: cl (CLose)
Command:

Continue as shown in Fig. 3.8 to complete the outline. The second method is:

Command:_pline
From point: 60,195
Current line width is 0

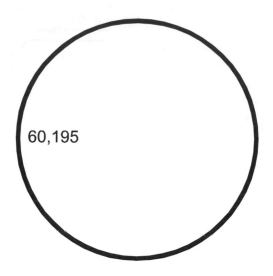

Fig. 3.8 **Polyline** circle
example

prompt sequence: w (Width)
Starting width <0>: 3
Ending width <3>: *right-click*
prompt sequence: a (Arc)
prompt sequence: r (Radius)
Radius: 80
Angle/<Endpoint>: @160,0
<Endpoint of arc>: @-160,0
<Endpoint of arc>: *right-click*
Command:

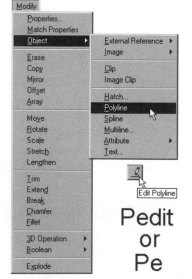

Fig. 3.9 Calling **Edit Polyline**

The Edit Polyline command

Polylines can be edited using the **Edit Polyline** command, usually
referred to as pedit. If pedit is used on a line, the line must first be
converted into a polyline.

   To call the tool *click* on its tool icon in the **Modify II** toolbar
(Release 12 toolbox), *click* on the name **Polyline** in the **Modify**
menu, or *enter* **pedit** or **pe** at the command line. (The easiest method
is to *enter* **pe** at the command line; see Fig. 3.9.) When the tool is
called the command line shows a number of prompts:

Command: *enter* pe *right-click*
Close/Join/Width/Edit vertex/Fit/Spline/Decurve/Undo/eXit <X>:

Only three of the prompts for editing will be demonstrated in the
following examples, but these three show the possibilities available with the command.

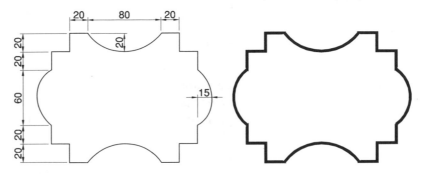

Fig. 3.10 Example 1

Pedit: example 1 (Fig. 3.10)

Construct the polyline outline shown in the left-hand drawing of Fig. 3.10 to a width of 0. (Do not attempt to include the dimensions shown in the illustration.) Then:

Command: pe
Select polyline: *pick* the polyline just constructed
prompt sequence: w (Width)
Enter width for all segments: 3
prompt sequence: *right-click*
Command:

The right-hand drawing of Fig. 3.10 shows the pline outline edited to the new width.

Pedit: example 2 (Fig. 3.11)

Construct the incomplete polyline outline given in the left-hand drawing of Fig. 3.11 to a width of 1. Then:

Command: pedit
PEDIT Select polyline: *pick* the pline just drawn
prompt sequence: c (Close)
Command:

The polyline closes as shown in the right-hand drawing of Fig. 3.11.

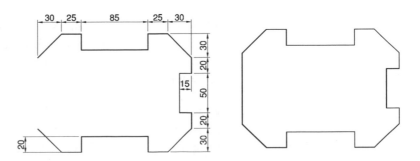

Fig. 3.11 Example 2

Pedit: example 3 (Fig. 3.12)

Construct the polyline outline shown in the left-hand drawing of Fig. 3.12 to a width of 2. Then:

Command: pedit
Select polyline: *pick* the polyline just constructed
prompt sequence: e (Edit vertex)
[A cross appears at the point 100,240 at which the pline was started.]
prompt sequence: *right-click* (to accept n for Next)
[The cross moves to the next vertex of the outline. Continue *right-clicks* until the cross is on the vertex of the angle at the right of the outline.]
prompt sequence: m (Move)
Enter new location: @50,0
prompt sequence: x (eXit) *right-click*
Command:

And the vertex is moved as shown in the right-hand drawing of Fig. 3.12.

Note

The prompt sequence when the response is **e** is:

Next/Previous/Break/Insert/Move/Regen/Straighten/Tangent/ Width/eXit <N>:

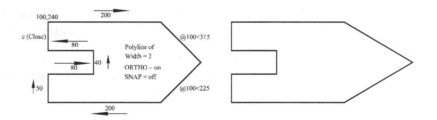

Fig. 3.12 Example 3

Questions

1. What are the differences between a line drawn with the aid of the command **Line** and a line drawn with the aid of **Polyline**?
2. What is *entered* at the command line to call the command **Polyline**?
3. How can arrows be constructed using the command **Polyline**?
4. What is meant by 'direct entry' construction?
5. How are the coordinates shown at top or bottom of the AutoCAD screen changed from showing absolute units to relative units?

6. Which command is *entered* to call the command **Edit Polyline**?
7. What is the purpose of the **Edit vertex** prompt of **Edit Polyline**?
8. Can you explain two methods of constructing circles with the aid of the **Polyline** command?
9. You have drawn a polyline of width 0. How can its width be changed to 2?
10. The prompt **Undo** can be seen in the **Polyline** prompt sequence. What is its purpose?

Exercises

1–3. Construct the outlines given in Figs 3.13–15 to a width of 2 using the command **Polyline**.

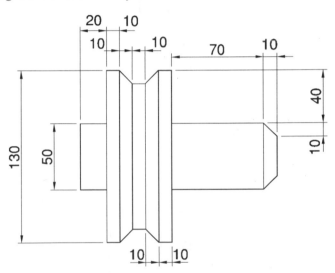

Fig. 3.13 Exercise 1

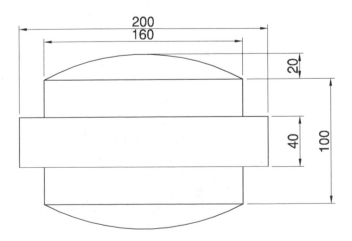

Fig. 3.14 Exercise 2

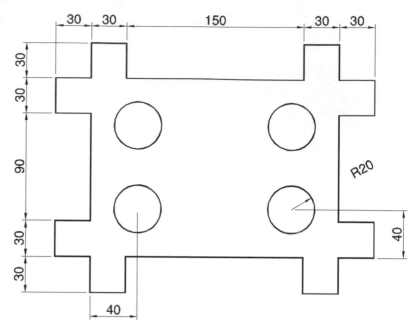

Fig. 3.15 Exercise 3

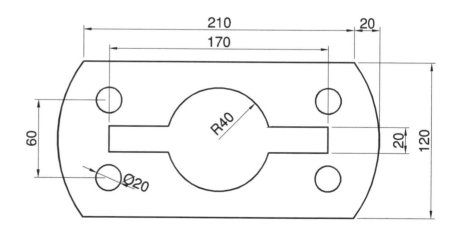

Fig. 3.16 Exercise 4

4. Construct the outline given in Fig. 3.16 to a width of 1.5 using the **Polyline** command. When completed, change the width of each part of your drawing so that the plines are of width 2.
5. Figure 3.17 shows front and end views of a pin. Construct the two views with the aid of the command **Polyline**. The end view (on the right) must be kept in horizontal alignment with the front view.
6. Construct the view of a plate given in Fig. 3.18 using the command **Polyline**. Use a line width of 0.8. Do not include dimensions.

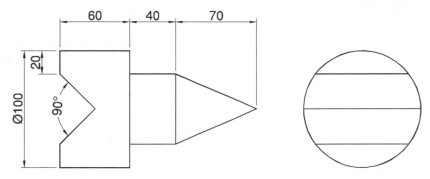

Fig. 3.17 Exercise 5

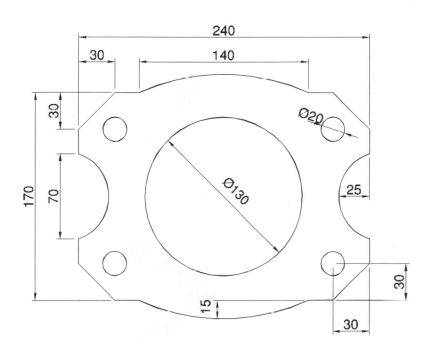

Fig. 3.18 Exercise 6

7. The upper drawing of Fig. 3.19 shows a double-ended arrow constructed with the aid of the command **Polyline**. Construct the double arrow. Then, with the aid of the command **Edit Polyline**, change your double arrow to the shape shown in the lower drawing of Fig. 3.19.

8. Construct the outline in Fig. 3.20 using the different pline widths as shown.

9. Using **Edit Polyline**, edit the drawing in your answer to Exercise 8 to appear as in Fig. 3.21.

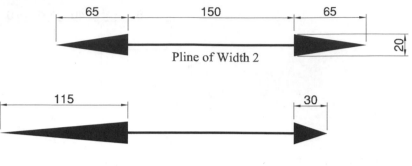

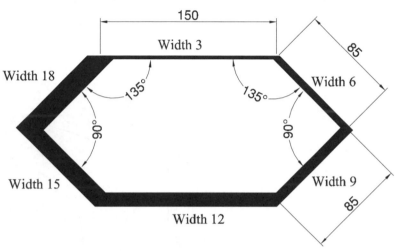

Fig. 3.19 Exercise 7

Fig. 3.20 Exercise 8

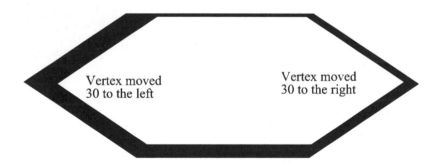

Fig. 3.21 Exercise 9

CHAPTER 4

Printing/plotting

Introduction

The method of printing or plotting a drawing shown here is restricted to the use of the Windows' default printer (loaded at the time Windows was set up). In the example shown here the default printer is a Hewlett Packard LaserJet, but it could be any other printer or plotter. Once a printer or plotter is set up to produce 'hardcopy' of drawings the method of printing is the same whichever printer or plotter is in use. As AutoCAD or AutoCAD LT has been updated one feature which has undergone constant improvement is the printing or plotting procedure.

Printing or plotting a drawing

The tool used for printing or plotting is the **Print** or **Plot** tool (depending upon the release of AutoCAD or AutoCAD LT). Up to Release 14 the tool was called **Print**, but with AutoCAD 2000 (and AutoCAD LT 2000) this was changed to **Plot** (see Fig. 4.1).

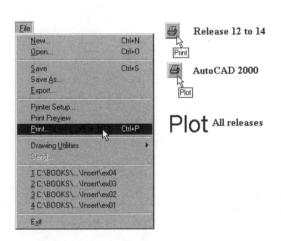

Fig. 4.1 Calling the **Print** or **Plot** tool

When the tool is called, either by *clicking* the tool icon or the **Print . . .** or **Plot . . .** menu item, a dialog box appears. In releases up to 14 this is the **Plot Configuration** or **Print/Plot Configuration** dialog box (Fig. 4.2), which remained largely unchanged between the three releases. In AutoCAD 2000 it is named **Plot**. It should also be noted that in AutoCAD 2000, the dialog box has two parts (the **Plot Settings** part is shown in Fig. 4.3).

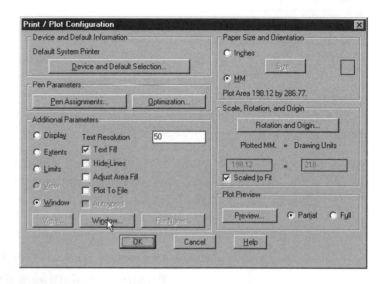

Fig. 4.2 **Print/Plot Configuration** dialog box

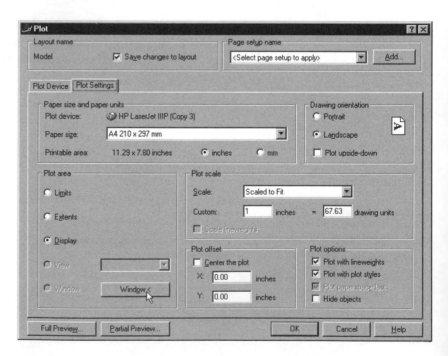

Fig. 4.3 **Plot** dialog box (AutoCAD 2000) with the **Plot Settings** tab showing

The example shown here uses the **Window** method of selecting the area of the AutoCAD window which is to be printed. The procedure is:

1. Open the **Plot** dialog box.
2. *Click* on the **Window<** button, which (up to Release 14) brings up the **Window Selection** dialog (Fig. 4.4). Then *click* on the **Pick<** button.
3. Prompts at the command line request corners for the window. *Pick* the two window corners. The **Window Selection** dialog reappears showing the coordinates of the corners of the window (Fig. 4.5).
4. *Click* on the **OK** button and the **Plot** dialog box reappears.
5. *Click* on the **Full Review** button and a review window showing how the hardcopy will look appears (Fig. 4.6).
6. Close the review window and *click* on the **OK** button of the **Plot** dialog box.
7. The drawing prints as indicated in the **Full Review** window.

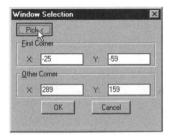

Fig. 4.4 **Window Selection** dialog box

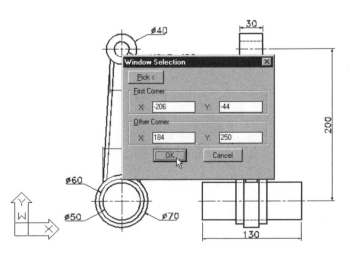

Fig. 4.5 **Window Selection** dialog box reappears after window corners have been *picked*

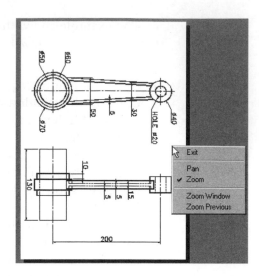

Fig. 4.6 **Full Review** window

Polygon, Rectangle and Ellipse tools

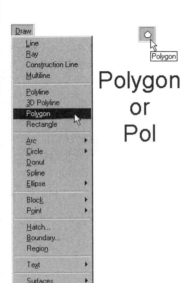

Fig. 5.2 Calling the **Polygon** tool

The Polygon tool

Six examples of polygons constructed with the aid of the **Polygon** tool are shown in Fig. 5.1. These have four, five, six and eight sides (their names are given in the figure). All except the bottom right-hand polygon have been constructed 'inscribed' within a circle; the last polygon has been constructed 'circumscribed' outside a circle. (It should be noted that the circles are only shown in Fig. 5.1 for clarity.)

To call the **Polygon** tool *click* on its icon in the **Draw** toolbar (Release 12 toolbox), *click* on its name in the **Draw** menu, or *enter* **polygon** or **pol** at the command line (Fig. 5.2). The command line shows the following (slightly different in AutoCAD 2000):

Command:_polygon
Number of sides <4>: *right-click*
Edge/<Center of polygon>: 65,240

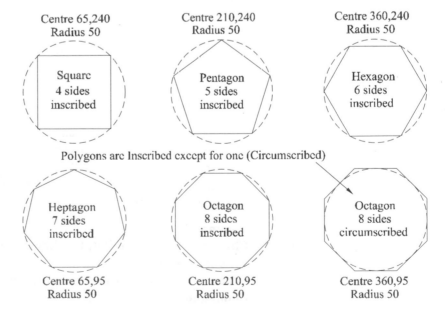

Fig. 5.1 Use of the **Polygon** tool

Inscribed in circle/Circumscribed around circle (I/C) <I>: *right-click*
Radius of circle: 50
Command:

Another example of using the Polygon tool

Figure 5.3 shows another example of using the **Polygon** tool. Start with a six-sided polygon (a hexagon) approximately centre on the screen with edges of length 120. Add six further hexagons centred at the vertices of the large hexagon with edges of length 60. Use the **end** osnap to centre the smaller polygons.

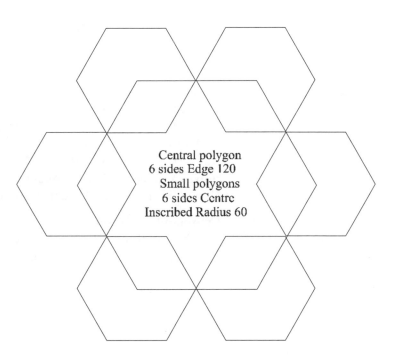

Central polygon
6 sides Edge 120
Small polygons
6 sides Centre
Inscribed Radius 60

Fig. 5.3 Use of the **Polygon**
tool

The Rectangle tool

To call the **Rectangle** tool *click* on its icon in the **Draw** toolbar, *click* on its name in the **Draw** menu, or *enter* **rectangle** or **rec** at the command line (Fig. 5.4). The tool is not available in Release 12 and in Release 13 the **Width**, **Fillet** and **Chamfer** prompts are not available. When the tool is called the command line shows:

Command:_rectangle
Chamfer/Elevation/Fillet/Thickness/Width<First corner>: *pick* or
    enter coordinates
Other corner: *pick* or *enter* coordinates
Command:

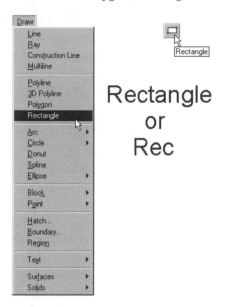

Fig. 5.4 Calling the **Rectangle** tool

Figure 5.5 shows several examples of rectangles constructed with the **Rectangle** tool. Note the differences in width, chamfer and fillet settings. (Note: an example of the **Elevation** and **Thickness** prompts is not included.)

Rectangle example (Fig. 5.5 bottom right drawing)

Command:_rectangle
Chamfer/Elevation/Fillet/Thickness/Width<First corner>: c (Chamfer)
First chamfer distance for rectangles <0>: 30
Second chamfer distance for rectangles <0>: 15
Chamfer/Elevation/Fillet/Thickness/Width<First corner>: w (Width)
Width for rectangles <0>: 5

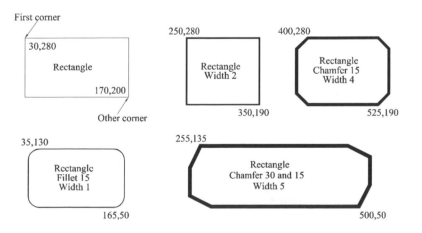

Fig. 5.5 Use of the **Rectangle** tool

Chamfer/Elevation/Fillet/Thickness/Width<First corner>: 255,135
Other corner: 500,50
Command:

The Ellipse tool

In geometric terms an ellipse is constructed on two axes: the 'major' axis and the 'minor' axis (see Fig. 5.7). An ellipse can also be regarded as a circular disc viewed face on and being rotated about a diameter. As the rotation angle increases to 90° the disc would be seen flatter and flatter until it is seen as a straight line.

To call the **Ellipse** tool *click* on its icon in the **Draw** toolbar (Release 12 toolbox), *click* on its name in the **Draw** menu, or *enter* **ellipse** or **el** at the command line (Fig. 5.6).

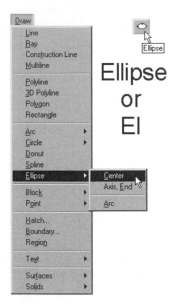

Fig. 5.6 Calling the **Ellipse** tool

Ellipse examples (Fig. 5.7)

Call the tool and the command line shows:

Command:_ellipse
Arc/Center/<Axis endpoint 1>: *enter* coordinates or *pick* a point
Axis endpoint 2: *enter* coordinates or *pick* a point
<Other axis distance>/Rotation: *enter* coordinates or *pick* a point
Command:

Or if the **Center** option is taken:

Command:_ellipse
Arc/Center/<Axis endpoint 1>: *enter* c (Center) *right-click*
Center of ellipse: *enter* coordinates or *pick* a point
Axis endpoint: *enter* coordinates or *pick* a point
<Other axis distance>/Rotation: *enter* coordinates or *pick* a point
Command:

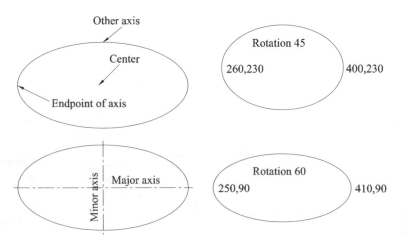

Fig. 5.7 Use of the **Ellipse** tool

Or if the **Rotation** option is taken:

Arc/Center/<Axis endpoint 1>: *enter* coordinates or *pick* a point
Axis endpoint 2: *enter* coordinates or *pick* a point
<Other axis distance>/Rotation: *enter* r (Rotation) *right-click*
Rotation around major axis: *enter* a figure *right-click*
Command:

Note: AutoCAD 2000

Many of the prompt sequences in AutoCAD 2000 are slightly different from those in other releases although this does not affect working methods. As an example the prompts for **Ellipse** in AutoCAD 2000 are as follows:

Command:_ellipse
Specify axis endpoint of ellipse or [Arc/Center]: *enter* coordinates or *pick* a point
Specify other endpoint of axis: *enter* coordinates or *pick* a point
Specify distance to other axis or [Rotation]: *enter* r (Rotation) *right-click*
Specify rotation around major axis: *enter* a figure *right-click*
Command:

Further Ellipse examples (Fig. 5.8)

Figure 5.8 shows four ellipses with the same axis lengths and sharing a common central point. The ellipses were drawn by using the relative coordinate entry method (length and angle) for determining the ends of the axes of each ellipse after having fixed the common central point for each ellipse. The relative coordinate entries are indicated with Fig. 5.8.

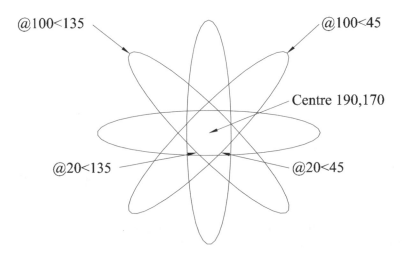

Fig. 5.8 Use of the **Ellipse** tool

Donut
or
Do

Fig. 5.9 Calling the **Donut** tool

The Donut tool

'Donuts' (doughnuts) are of value when wishing to show such features as intersecting electrical connections in a circuit diagram. They also can be used for drawing circles with thick (wide) outlines when required. To call the tool, *click* on the name **Donut** in the **Draw** menu or *enter* **donut** or **do** at the command line. The inner and outer diameters of the donut have to be set before the donut can be placed in a drawing. When the tool is called, the command line shows:

Command_donut
Inside diameter <0>: *enter* the required figure
Outside diameter <1>: *enter* the required figure
Center of doughnut: the ghosted donut appears at the intersection of the cursor hairs and can be placed in any required position, either by *picking* or by *entering* coordinates; donuts with the same inner and outer diameters can then be placed one after another, until *right-clicking* or pressing **Return** ends the sequence.

Figure 5.10 shows a number of donuts with different inner and outer diameters.

Note

To turn the **Fill** tool on or off:

Command: *enter* fill *right-click*
ON/OFF <ON>: *enter* off *right-click* if **Fill** is to be turned off.

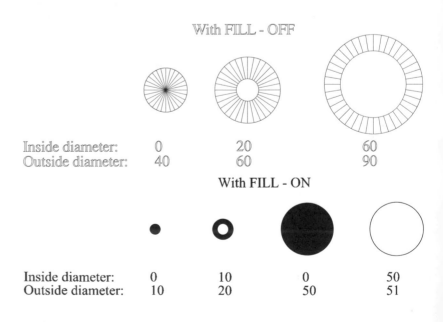

With FILL - OFF

| Inside diameter: | 0 | 20 | 60 |
| Outside diameter: | 40 | 60 | 90 |

With FILL - ON

Fig. 5.10 Use of the **Donut** tool, with **Fill** on and off

| Inside diameter: | 0 | 10 | 0 | 50 |
| Outside diameter: | 10 | 20 | 50 | 51 |

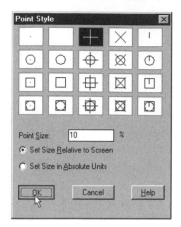

Fig. 5.11 **Point Style** dialog box

Fig. 5.12 Use of the **Point** tool

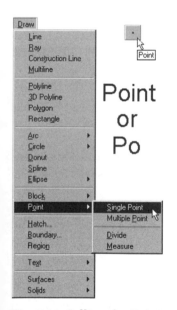

Fig. 5.13 Calling the **Point** tool

The Point tool

In any of the releases *entering* **ddptype** at the command line makes the **Point Style** dialog box appear (Fig. 5.11). Here a style of point can be selected along with the size at which the selected point is to appear on screen.

Figure 5.12 shows a number of points of different styles placed on screen. To call the tool, first select the required point style and its size from the **Point Style** dialog box, then *click* on its icon in the **Draw** toolbar, *click* on its name in the **Draw** menu, or *enter* **point** or **po** at the command line (Fig. 5.13):

Command:_point Point: *pick* a point or *enter* coordinates.

Any number of points of the desired style can be placed one after another, until a *right-clicking* or pressing **Return** ends the sequence.

A worked example

In this worked example (Fig. 5.14) all prompt sequences are shown in full and the tools **Rectangle**, **Polygon**, **Circle** and **Ellipse** are used to construct a drawing. Note the following:

1. This example is only fully possible using Release 14 and AutoCAD 2000, because **Width** and **Fillet** are not available with the **Rectangle** tool in earlier releases.
2. From Release 13 onwards ellipses are true, accurate objects, which cannot be edited with the **Edit Polyline** tool. In this example the width of the line of the central ellipse in the drawing has been

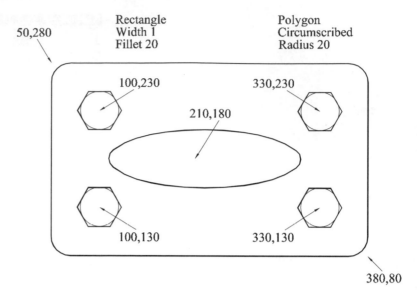

Fig. 5.14 Worked example

changed with the aid of the **Edit Polyline** tool from **0** to **1**. This has been made possible by calling the set variable **PELLIPSE** and setting the variable to **1** as follows:

Command: *enter* pellipse
New value for PELLIPSE <0>: *enter* 1 *right-click*
Command:

3. *Enter* and *right-click* are not shown in the following sequences, except when acceptance of the prompt is necessary, in which case *right-click* will be included.

Using Release 14 or AutoCAD 2000, the sequence of calls and responses for this example are:

1. Call the **Rectangle** tool:

Command:_rectangle
Chamfer/Elevation/Fillet/Thickness/Width<First corner>: w (Width)
Width for rectangles <0>: 1
Chamfer/Elevation/Fillet/Thickness/Width<First corner>: f (Fillet)
Fillet radius for rectangles<0>: 20
Chamfer/Elevation/Fillet/Thickness/Width<First corner>: 50,280
Other corner: 380,80
Command:

2. Call the **Polygon** tool:

Command:_polygon Number of sides <4>: 6
Edge/<Center of polygon>: 100,280

Inscribed in circle/Circumscribed about circle (I/C) <I>:
Radius of circle: 20
Command: *right-click* (repeats **Polygon**)
POLYGON Number of sides <4>: 6
Chamfer/Elevation/Fillet/Thickness/Width<First corner>: *right-click*
Edge/<Center of polygon>: 330,230
Inscribed in circle/Circumscribed about circle (I/C) <C>: *right-click*
Radius of circle: 20
Command: *right-click*
POLYGON Number of sides <4>: 6
Chamfer/Elevation/Fillet/Thickness/Width<First corner>: *right-click*
Edge/<Center of polygon>: 100,130
Inscribed in circle/Circumscribed about circle (I/C) <C>: *right-click*
Radius of circle: 20
Command: *right-click*
POLYGON Number of sides <4>: 6
Chamfer/Elevation/Fillet/Thickness/Width<First corner>: *right-click*
Edge/<Center of polygon>: 330,130
Inscribed in circle/Circumscribed about circle (I/C) <C>: *right-click*
Radius of circle: 20
Command:

3. Call the **Edit Polyline** tool:

Command:_pedit Select polyline
prompts sequence: W (Width)
prompts sequence: 1
prompts sequence: *right-click*
Command: *right-click*

Repeat for the other three polygons.

4. Call the **Circle** tool:

Command_circle 3P/2P/TTR/<Center point>: 100,230
Diameter/<Radius>: 20
Command: *right-click*

Repeat for the other three circles centred at the centres of the polygons.

5. Call the **PELLIPSE** variable:

Command: *enter* pellipse
New value for PELLIPSE <0>: *enter* 1 *right-click*
Command:

6. Call the **Ellipse** tool:

Command:_ellipse
Arc/Center/<Axis endpoint 1>: c
Center of ellipse: 210,180
Axis endpoint: *drag* the cursor horizontally to the left and *enter*
   90 and *right-click*
<Other axis endpoint>/Rotation: *drag* the cursor vertically up-
   wards and *enter* 30 and *right-click*
Command:

7. With **Edit Polyline** change the width of the ellipse line to **1**.

Questions

1. Some of the abbreviations for tool names used in this book are not available as standard in AutoCAD Releases 12 and 13. It is however possible for the reader to make changes to a file in the AutoCAD directories to allow any abbreviation to be used. What are the steps needed to make such abbreviations available when working in these two releases?
2. What are the abbreviations for the commands **Polygon**, **Rectangle**, **Ellipse**, **Donut** and **Point**?
3. The prompts available in AutoCAD Release 14 and AutoCAD 2000 for the **Rectangle** tool are not the same as prompts available in Releases 12 and 13. What are the differences between these?
4. One example of the difference between the prompts sequence for AutoCAD 2000 and earlier releases is given in this chapter. Have you noted this difference? Do you think it alters methods of working between releases?
5. What is the purpose of the set variable **PELLIPSE**?
6. How is this variable set on or off?
7. What is the difference between inscribed and circumscribed polygons?
8. What are the names of the axes of an ellipse?
9. When using the **Donut** tool what is the effect of turning the set variable **FILL** off?
10. How is the **Point Style** dialog box called to screen? Have you noted any other method in the AutoCAD you are using for calling the dialog box?

Exercises

1. Figure 5.15 shows a plate made from 10 mm thick steel to be bolted in position onto a container. Working to the dimensions given with the drawing make an accurate drawing of the plate and its bolt heads. Do not attempt to include the dimensions.

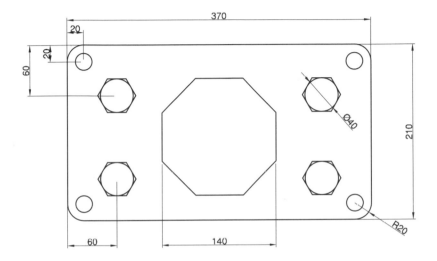

Fig. 5.15 Exercise 1

2. Figure 5.16 shows four identical rectangles all centred in the AutoCAD drawing area. Construct the four rectangles.
3. Construct the drawing given in Fig. 5.17. When completed change the line thickness of each part from **0** to **1**.

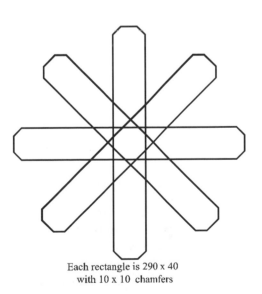

Each rectangle is 290 x 40
with 10 x 10 chamfers

Fig. 5.16 Exercise 2

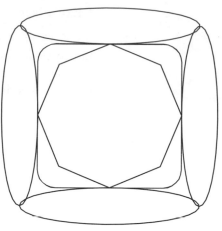

Ellipses are 200 x 20. Rectangle
is filleted radius 20. Polygon is
inscribed in a circle.

Fig. 5.17 Exercise 3

4. Figure 5.18 shows a 'face' constructed with the aid of the
Rectangle, **Ellipse** and **Donut** tools. Working to the given dimensions construct the given drawing. Do not attempt to include any
of the dimensions.

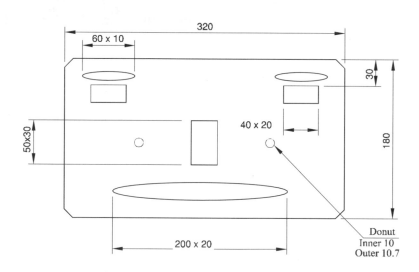

Fig. 5.18 Exercise 4

5. Figure 5.19 shows the connectors for an electric circuit with
donuts at intersecting connectors and at the ends of connectors
where parts are to be connected. Working to the given dimensions construct the drawing. Do not attempt to include any of
the dimensions.

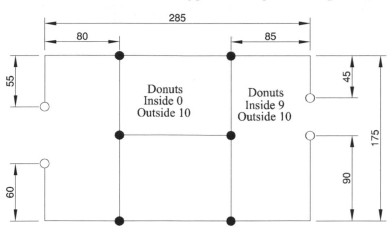

Fig. 5.19 Exercise 5

CHAPTER 6

Some Modify tools

Introduction

In this chapter examples of using the tools **Move**, **Copy**, **Trim**, **Offset**, **Mirror** and **Rotate** will be shown. These tools can be found either in the **Construct** menu and the **Modify** menu in Releases 12 and 13, or in the single **Modify** menu in Release 14 and AutoCAD 2000. (Illustrations featuring menus in this chapter show the Release 14 menu.) From Release 13 onwards the tool icons for these tools are the same, but in Release 12 they do not have the same shapes. Both the Release 12 icons and icons from later releases will be shown in illustrations (from the Release 12 the toolbox, or from the toolbars in later releases (including tooltips)). The tools are also available in all releases of AutoCAD LT.

Note

If running Releases 12 or 13 it must be remembered that the abbreviations for tool names shown in this chapter may need to be added to the **acad.pgp** file.

The Move tool

To call the **Move** tool, *click* on its tool icon, *click* its name in the **Modify** menu, or *enter* **move** or **m** at the command line (Fig. 6.1).

Move: example 1 (Fig. 6.2)

In Fig. 6.2 the circle to the left of the ellipse has been placed in the wrong position. To move the circle to its correct position within the ellipse call the **Move** tool:

Command:_move
Select objects: *pick* the circle **1 found**
Select objects: *right-click*
Base point or displacement: *pick* the circle centre

Fig. 6.1 Calling the **Move** tool

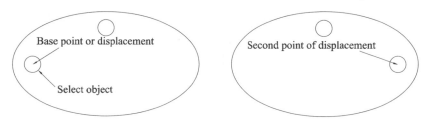

Fig. 6.2 Example 1

Second point of displacement: *pick* the new position for the circle
  centre
Command:

Fig. 6.3 Example 2

Move: example 2 (Fig. 6.3)

Command:_move
Select objects: w (Window)
First corner: *pick* **Opposite corner:** *pick* **4 found**
Select objects: *right-click*
Base point or displacement: *pick*
Second point of displacement: *pick*
Command:

Note

When using the **w** command, either **Other corner** or **Opposite
corner** will appear as the prompt, depending upon which release
of AutoCAD you are using.

The Copy tool

To call the **Copy** tool, *click* on its tool icon, *click* on its name in
the **Construct** (Releases 13 and 13) or in the **Modify** menu (Release 14
and AutoCAD 2000), or *enter* **copy** or **cp** at the command line
(Fig. 6.4).

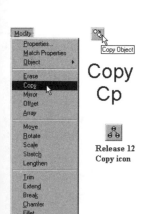

Fig. 6.4 Calling the **Copy** tool

Copy: example 1 (Fig. 6.5)

Command:_copy
Select objects: w (Window)
First corner: *pick* **Opposite corner:** *pick* **8 found**
Select objects: *right-click*
<Base point or displacement>/Multiple: *pick*
Second point of displacement: *pick*
Command:

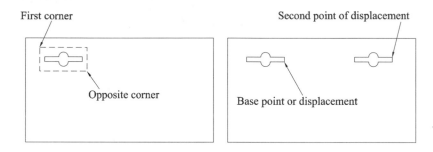

Fig. 6.5 Example 1

Copy: example 2 (Fig. 6.6)

Command:_copy
Select objects: *pick* (the outline is a closed pline) **1 found**
Select objects: *right-click*
<Base point or displacement>/Multiple: m (Multiple)
Base point: *pick*
Second point of displacement: *pick*
Second point of displacement: *pick*
Second point of displacement: *pick*
Second point of displacement: *pick*
Second point of displacement: *right-click*
Command:

Note

Once again it needs to be remembered that the prompts in AutoCAD 2000 are worded slightly differently, but that the results are the same.

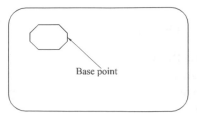
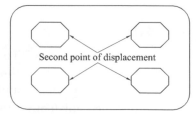

Fig. 6.6 Example 2

Fig. 6.7 Calling the **Trim** tool

The Trim tool

To call the **Trim** tool, *click* on its tool icon in the **Modify** toolbar, *click* on its name in the **Modify** menu, or *enter* **trim** or **tr** at the command line (Fig. 6.7).

Trim: example 1 (Fig. 6.8)

Command:_trim
Select cutting edges: (Projmode = UCS, Edgemode = Extend): *pick*
Select objects: *pick* **1 found** (the three 'lines' are a polyline)
Select objects: *right-click*
Select object to trim: *pick*
Select object to trim: *pick*
<Select object to trim>/Project/Edge/Undo: *pick*
<Select object to trim>/Project/Edge/Undo: *pick*
<Select object to trim>/Project/Edge/Undo: *right-click*
Command:

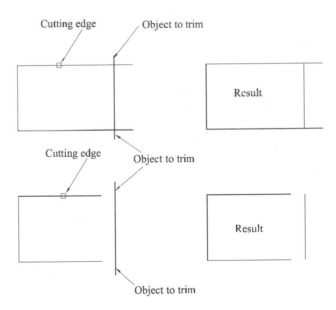

Fig. 6.8 Example 1

Note

It will be seen from the lower pair of drawings in Fig. 6.8 that trimming will occur to an imaginary edge – that is an extension of the parts to which objects can be trimmed.

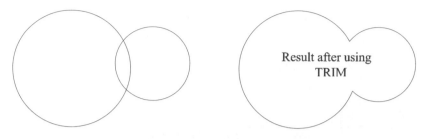

Fig. 6.9 Example 2

Trim: example 2 (Fig. 6.9)

Draw two intersecting circles of any radius as shown in the left-hand drawing of Fig. 6.9. Call the **Trim** tool and first trim back the smaller circle to the larger, followed by trimming the larger to the arc left after trimming the smaller.

The Offset tool

To call the **Offset** tool, *click* on its tool icon, *click* on its name in the **Construct** menu (Releases 12 or 13) or the **Modify** menu (Release 14 and AutoCAD 2000), or *enter* **offset** or **o** at the command line (Fig. 6.10).

Offset examples (Fig. 6.11)

Command:_offset
Offset distance or Through <Through>: 10
Select object to offset: *pick*
Side to offset? *pick*
Select object to offset: *pick*

Fig. 6.10 Calling the **Offset** tool

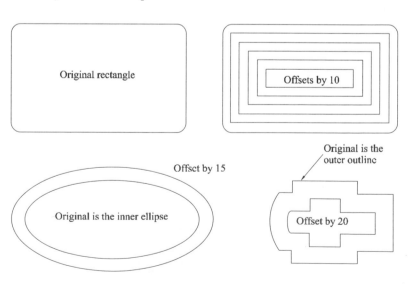

Fig. 6.11 Use of the **Offset** tool

Side to offset? *pick*
Select object to offset: *pick*
Side to offset? *pick*
Select object to offset: *pick*
Side to offset? *pick* **Select object to offset:** *pick*
Side to offset? *pick*

And so on until the requisite number of offsets have been made, then *right-click*.

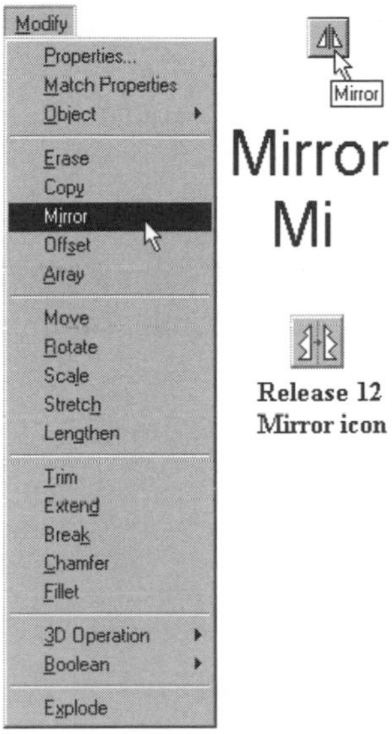

The Mirror tool

To call the **Mirror** tool, *click* on its tool icon, *click* on its name in the **Construct** menu (Releases 12 or 13) or the **Modify** menu (Release 14 and AutoCAD 2000), or *enter* **mirror** or **mi** at the command line (Fig. 6.12).

Mirror examples (Figs 6.13 and 6.14)

Command:_mirror
Select objects: *pick*
Select objects: *right-click*
First point on mirror line: *pick* **Second point:** *pick*
Delete old objects? <N>: *right-click*
Command:

Command:_mirror
Select objects: w
First corner: *pick* **Other corner:** *pick* **9 found**
Select objects: *right-click*
First point on mirror line: *pick* **Second point:** *pick*
Delete old objects? <N>: *right-click*
Command:

Fig. 6.12 Calling the **Mirror** tool

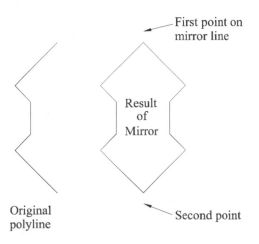

Fig. 6.13 Example 1

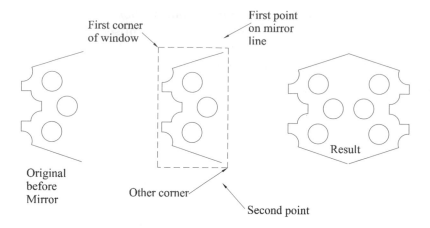

Fig. 6.14 Example 2

Fig. 6.15 Calling the **Rotate** tool

Rotate
Ro

Release 12
Rotate icon

The Rotate tool

To call the **Rotate** tool, *click* on its tool icon, *click* on its name in the **Modify** menu, or *enter* **rotate** or **ro** at the command line (Fig. 6.15).

Rotate: example 1 (Fig. 6.16)

Command:_rotate
Select objects: *pick* or window the objects
Select objects: *right-click*
Base point: *pick*
<Rotation angle>/Reference: 30
Command:

Note

Figure 6.16 shows rotations at angles 30° 60°, 90°, 120°, 150°, 180°, 210° and 240°. Note the rotation is counter-clockwise (anticlockwise).

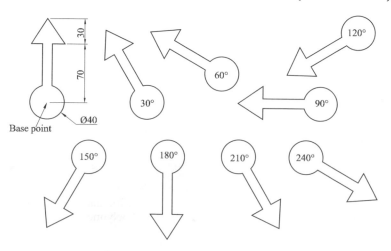

Fig. 6.16 Example 1

Rotate: example 2 (Fig. 6.17)

Command:_rotate
Select objects: *pick* or window the objects
Select objects: *right-click*
Base point: *pick*
<Rotation angle>/Reference: r
Reference angle <0>: 30
New angle: 45
Command:

Note

When using the **Reference** prompt, the reference angle shows in a 'ghosted' form before the new angle is formed (Fig. 6.17). Note that the new angle rotates anticlockwise from the reference angle.

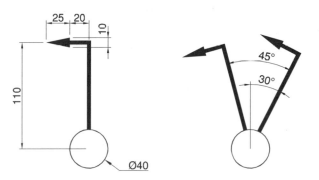

Fig. 6.17 Example 2

Summary

1. Remember there are no tooltips with Release 12 tool icons.
2. When using Releases 12 and 13 it will usually be necessary to add some of the abbreviations shown in this chapter to the **acad.pgp** file.
3. The prompts in AutoCAD 2000 vary somewhat from those of earlier releases, but this does not affect methods of working shown throughout this chapter.
4. The AutoCAD 2000 prompts frequently use the words **Specify** rather than **Select** and include some new and more advanced prompts.
5. The **Move**, **Trim** and **Rotate** tools can be selected from the **Modify** menu no matter which release is in use. The other three tools (**Copy**, **Offset** and **Mirror**) are found in the **Construct** menu in Releases 12 and 13.

Questions

1. If you are working in Release 12, in which menu would you find the **Move** tool?
2. If working with Release 13 in which menu would you find the **Rotate** tool?
3. If when using the **Rotate** tool you decide to make use of the **Reference** prompt, why would you expect to have to *enter* two angle sizes?
4. If you wish to make several copies of part of a drawing how do you use the **Copy** tool?
5. If you are using the **Trim** tool in Releases 12 or 13 you will be unable to trim against a projected edge. Is it possible to overcome this problem when using these releases?

Exercises

1. Figure 6.18 – follow the procedure:

   (a) Copy drawing **1**.
   (b) Drawing **2**: with **Trim**, trim the circle to the two lines.
   (c) Drawing **3**: **Mirror** the semicircle and lines to the opposite edge.
   (d) Drawing **4**: **Copy**, **Rotate** and **Move** one of the semicircles and lines to either the left or right edge of the rectangle. Then **Mirror** the copy to the other edge. Finally **Trim** the rectangle edges to the semicircle and line group.

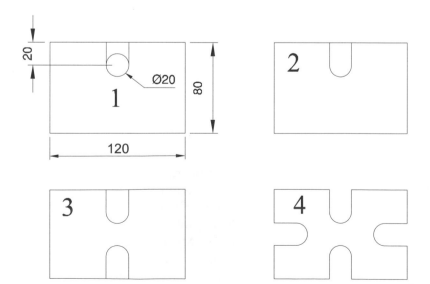

Fig. 6.18 Exercise 1

2. Figure 6.19: follow the procedure:

   (a) Copy drawing **1**.
   (b) Drawing **2**: with **Trim**, trim the circle back to the lines; with **Pedit** change the outline to a polyline.
   (c) Drawing **3**: **Offset** the outline by 5 internally.
   (d) Drawing **4**: use **Undo** to undo the offset; then **Offset** by 10 internally.

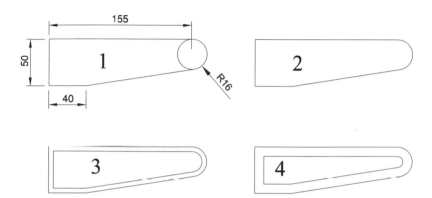

Fig. 6.19 Exercise 2

3. Figure 6.20: proceed as follows:

   (a) Drawing **1**: construct the drawing to the given dimensions; use the **TTR** prompt of the **Circle** tool.
   (b) Drawing **2**: using **Trim**, trim the circles against the outline.
   (c) Drawing **3**: using **Trim** again, trim the outline against the remainder of the circles; with **Pedit** change the outline to a polyline.
   (d) Drawing **4**: with **Offset**, offset internally by 5 units.

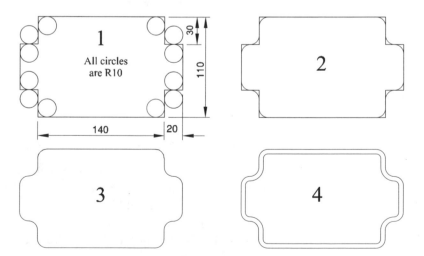

Fig. 6.20 Exercise 3

4. Figure 6.21: construct drawing **1** to the given dimensions, then:

   (a) Drawing **2**: with **Offset**, offset lines and circles by 5 internally.
   (b) Drawing **3**: with **Trim**, trim lines against the circles.

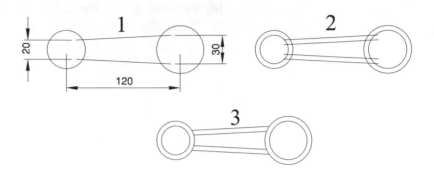

Fig. 6.21 Exercise 4

5. Figure 6.22: Construct drawing **1**, then:

   (a) Drawing **2**: **Offset** internally by 5.
   (b) Drawing **3**: **Mirror** the two outlines.
   (c) Drawing **4**: join the top and bottom points with a pline, then **Trim** unwanted lines.

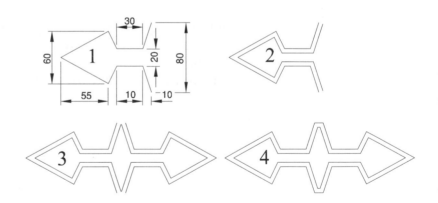

Fig. 6.22 Exercise 5

6. Figure 6.23: Construct drawing **1**, then:

   (a) Drawing **3**: **Copy** and **Rotate** the outline.
   (b) Drawing **4**: **Move** drawing 2 to the centre of drawing 3.
   (c) Drawing **5**: **Trim** unwanted parts.
   (d) Drawing **6**: construct the given rectangle around drawing 5.
   (e) **Move** the outline to the right-hand side of the rectangle.

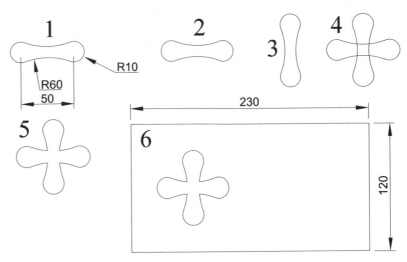

Fig. 6.23 Exercise 6

7. Figure 6.24 is a two-view orthographic projection of the slide part shown in an isometric view Fig. 6.25 (see Chapters 12 and 13 about orthographic and isometric views). Construct the drawing in Fig. 6.24 to the given dimensions.

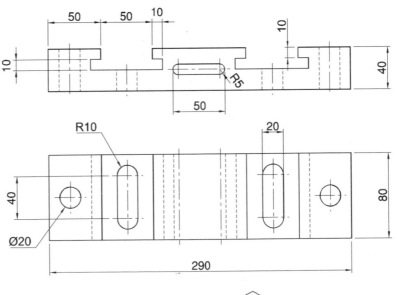

Fig. 6.24 Exercise 7

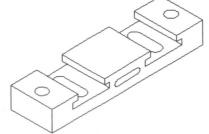

Fig. 6.25 Isometric drawing of the part shown in Fig. 6.24

8. Figure 6.26: construct the four circles of drawing **1** to the given dimensions, then:

(a) **Trim** the circles to produce drawing **2**; with **Pedit** join the trimmed parts as a single pline.

(b) With **Copy** using the **Multiple** prompt, construct the columns and rows of copies shown in drawing **3**.

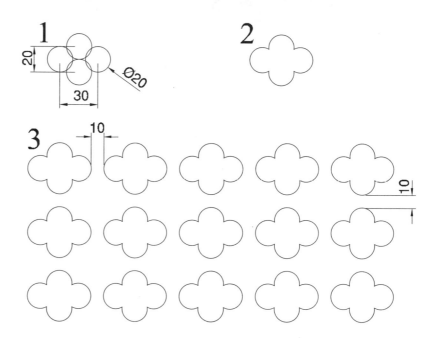

Fig. 6.26 Exercise 8

CHAPTER 7

Zooms and more Modify tools

The Zoom tool

As can be seen from Fig. 7.1 there are a variety of methods of calling the **Zoom** tool. However the quickest and easiest method of activating **Zoom** is to *enter* **z** at the command line in any AutoCAD release (including AutoCAD LT) followed by *entering* the initial or initials of the required prompt. The prompts resulting from calling **Zoom** in this manner vary slightly between releases, but not sufficiently to cause any problems in following the details given in this book. When a **z** (or **zoom**) is *entered* at the command line prompts show as follows for each of the four releases. Note that

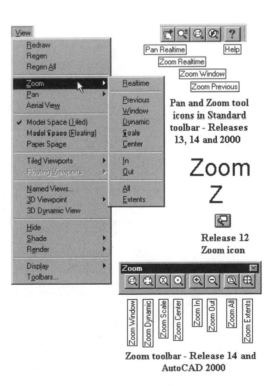

Fig. 7.1 Calling the **Zoom** tool

there will be a similarity to what is shown below when working in AutoCAD LT.

AutoCAD Release 12

Command: z
All/Center/Dynamic/Extents/Left/Previous/Vmax/Window/<Scale (X/XP)>:

AutoCAD Release 13

Command: z
All/Center/Dynamic/Extents/Left/Previous/Vmax/Window/<Scale (X/XP)>:

AutoCAD Release 14

Command: z
All/Center/Dynamic/Extents/Left/Previous/Scale (X/XP)/Window/ <real time>:

AutoCAD 2000

Command: z
[All/Center/Dynamic/Extents/Left/Previous/Scale/Window]<real time>:

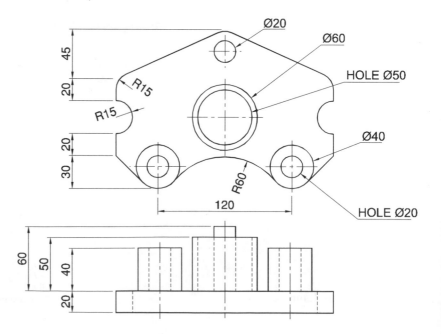

Fig. 7.2 Sample drawing used in the **Zoom** examples

Examples of zooms

Figures 7.3–7.7 show examples of the results of calling **Zoom**, followed by *entering* or *picking* the required zoom method. The examples are from the four releases of AutoCAD and from AutoCAD LT 98. The same drawing (Fig. 7.2) has been used in all five examples.

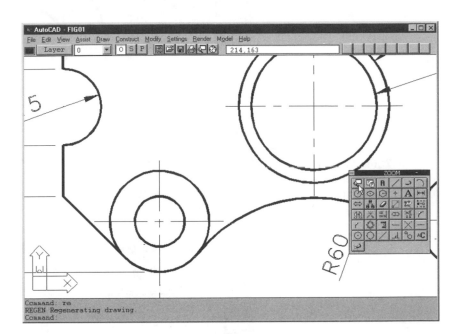

Fig. 7.3 **Zoom** Window
(Release 12)

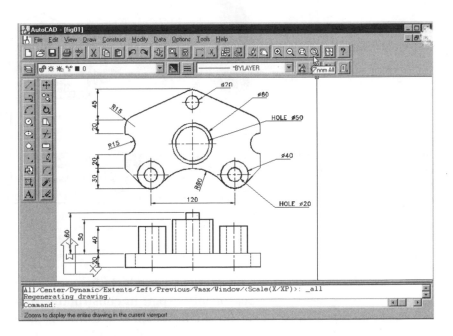

Fig. 7.4 **Zoom** All
(Release 13)

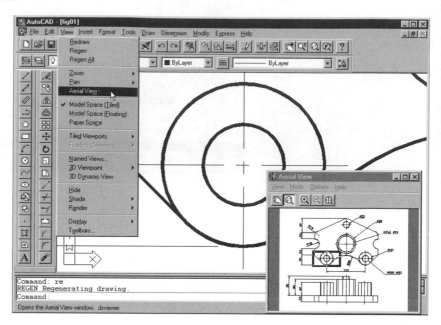

Fig. 7.5 **Zoom** Window (Release 14) together with the **Aerial View** window

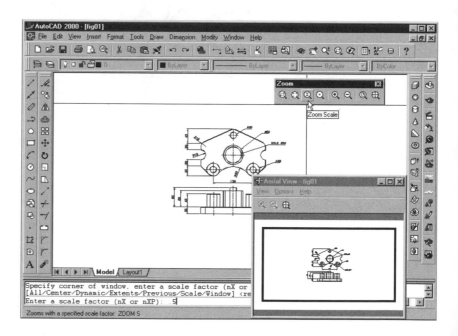

Fig. 7.6 **Zoom** Scale (0.5) (AutoCAD 2000), together with the **Aerial View** window

Note

The **Zoom** tool will be in frequent use by all those wishing to become reasonably expert in constructing drawings in AutoCAD. By using it the smallest area of a drawing can be precisely constructed.

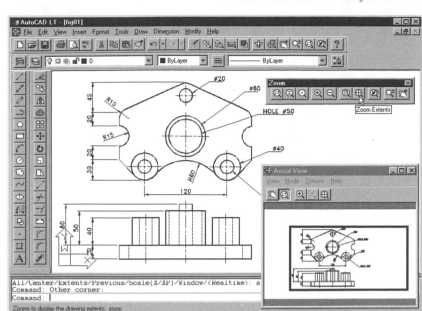

Fig. 7.7 **Zoom** Extents
(AutoCAD LT 98), together
with the **Aerial View**
window and the **Zoom**
toolbar

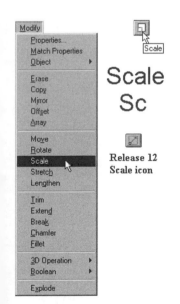

Fig. 7.8 Calling the **Scale** tool

The Scale tool

To call the **Scale** tool, *click* on its icon, *click* on its name in the **Modify** menu, or *enter* **sc** or **scale** at the command line (Fig. 7.8). When the tool is called, the command line shows:

Command:_scale
Select objects:

Scale: example 1 (Fig. 7.9)

1. Construct drawing **1** of Fig. 7.9.
2. **Copy** the drawing four times.
3. With the copy (drawing **2**) call the **Scale** tool:

   Command:_scale
   Select objects: w
   First corner: *pick* **Other corner:** *pick* **4 found**
   Select objects: *right-click*
   Base point: *pick*
   <Scale factor>/Reference: 0.5
   Command:

4. Scale the other three copies to 1.25 (drawing **3**), 0.75 (drawing **4**) and 1.5 (drawing **5**).

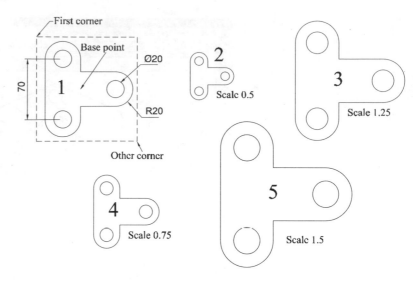

Fig. 7.9 Example 1

Scale: example 2 (Fig. 7.10)

Command:_scale
Select objects: w
First corner: *pick* **Other corner:** *pick* **4 found**
Select objects: *right-click*
Base point: *pick*
<Scale factor>/Reference: r
Reference length <1>: *right-click*
New length: 1.5
Command:

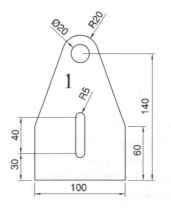

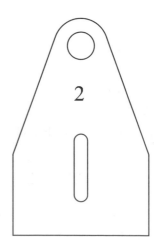

Fig. 7.10 Example 2

Break

Br

Release 12
Break icon

Fig. 7.11 Calling the
Break tool

The Break tool

To call the **Break** tool, *click* on its tool icon, *click* on its name in the **Modify** menu, or *enter* **br** or **break** at the command line (Fig. 7.11). When the tool is called, the command line shows:

Command:_break
Select object:

Break examples (Fig. 7.12)

1. Drawing **1**: draw a pline rectangle of any size.
2. Call **Break**:

   Command:_break
   Select object: *pick* a point at the start of the break
   Enter second point (or F for first point): *pick* the end of the break
   Command:

   The result is given in drawing **2** of Fig. 7.12.
3. Drawing **3**: draw a circle of any radius.
4. Call **Break**:

   Command:_break
   Select object: *pick* a point at the start of the break
   Enter second point (or F for first point): *pick* the end of the break
   Command:

   The result is shown in drawing **4** of Fig. 7.12. Note that it is necessary to select the second point in a counter-clockwise (anticlockwise) direction from the first point when you break a circle.

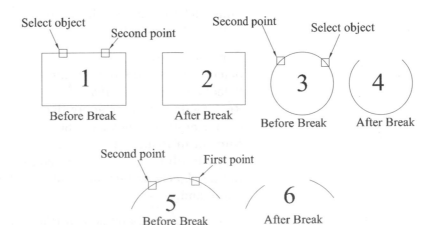

Fig. 7.12 **Break** example

5. Drawing **5**: draw an arc of any size.
6. Call **Break**:

> **Command:_break**
> **Select object:** *pick* the arc
> **Enter second point (or F for first point):** f
> **Enter first point:** *pick*
> **Enter second point:** *pick*
> **Command:**

The result is given in drawing **6** of Fig. 7.12.

Fig. 7.13 Calling the **Array** tool

The Array tool

To call the **Array** tool, *click* on its tool icon, *click* on its name in the **Construct** menu (Releases 12 and 13) or the **Modify** menu (Release 14 and AutoCAD 2000), or *enter* **ar** or **array** at the command line (Fig. 7.13). When the tool is called, the command line shows:

Command:_array
Select objects:

Note

1. There are two types of arrays: 'rectangular' in which the array is arranged in rows and columns, and 'polar' in which the array is circular formed around a central point.
2. When *entering* figures for the distance between rows, it must be remembered that unit distances in the Y direction are *negative* for an array *down* the screen.

Polar array: example 1 (Fig. 7.14)

Construct the outline shown in the top-left drawing of Fig. 7.14. Call the **Array** tool:

Command:_array
Select objects: *pick* the outline
Select objects: *right-click*
Rectangular or Polar array (R/P)<R>: p
Center of array: *pick* 210,160
Number of items: 12
Angle to fill (+=ccw, -= cw) <360>: *right-click*
Rotate objects as they are copied? <Y>: *right-click*
Command:

The array appears on screen (Fig. 7.14).

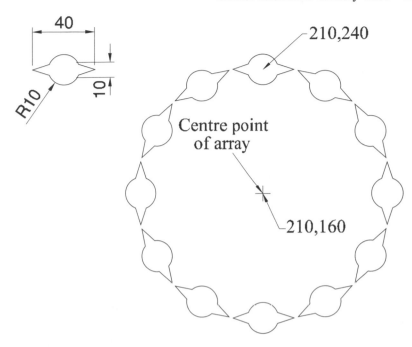

Fig. 7.14 Example 1

Rectangular array example (Fig. 7.15)

Construct the drawing on the left of the array. Call **Array**:

Command:_array
Select objects: *pick* the two outlines
Select objects: *right-click*
Rectangular or Polar array (R/P)<P>: r
Number of rows (—)<1>: 3
Number of columns (| | |): 5
Unit cell or distance between rows (—): 80
Distance between columns (| | |): 50
Command:

The rectangular array forms (Fig. 7.15).

Polar array: example 2 (Fig. 7.16)

Construct the outline shown in the drawing on the left of Fig. 7.16.
Call the **Array** tool:

Command:_array
Select objects: w
First corner: *pick* **Other corner:** *pick* **3 found**
Select objects: *right-click*
Rectangular or Polar array (R/P)<R>: r
Center of array: *pick*

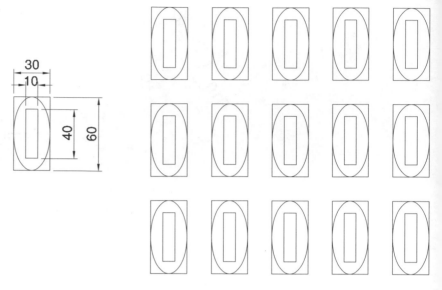

Fig. 7.15 Example 2

Number of items: 6
Angle to fill (+=ccw, -= cw) <360>: -180
Rotate objects as they are copied ? <Y>: n
Command:

The array appears on screen (Fig. 7.16).

Note

1. The response to the prompt **Angle to fill** is negative. This is because the default rotation in AutoCAD is anticlockwise. In this example the required rotation is clockwise, hence the negative figure of −180.

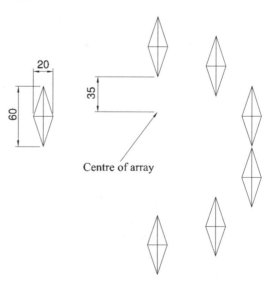

Fig. 7.16 Example 3

Fig. 7.17 Calling the **Stretch** tool

2. The response to the prompt **Rotate objects as they are copied?** is **n** (for **No**) because in this example the objects are not rotated when the array is constructed.
3. Both rectangular and polar arrays are of value in the construction of technical drawings using AutoCAD. This is emphasised in some of the exercises at the end of this chapter.

The Stretch tool

To call the **Stretch** tool, *click* on its tool icon, *click* on its name in the **Modify** menu, or *enter* **s** or **stretch** at the command line (Fig. 7.17). When the tool is called, the command line shows:

Command:_stretch
Select objects to stretch by crossing-window or crossing-polygon . . .
Select objects: c (for crossing-window)

Stretch examples (Fig. 7.18)

1. Construct drawing **1**: use a **Polyline** of width 1.
2. Call **Stretch**:

    Command:_stretch
    Select objects to stretch by crossing-window or crossing-polygon . . .
    Select objects: c
    First corner: *pick* **Other corner:** *pick* **1 found**
    Select objects: *right-click*
    Base point or displacement: *pick*

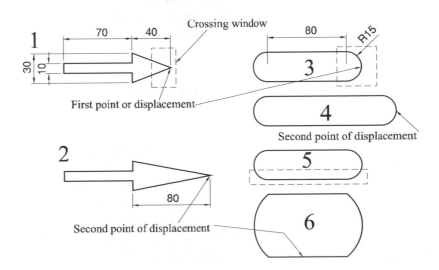

Fig. 7.18 **Stretch** examples

Second point of displacement: *pick*
Command:

The result is shown in drawing **2** of Fig. 7.18.

3. Construct drawing **3** of Fig. 7.18.
4. Call **Stretch** and *pick* a crossing-window as shown in drawing **3**. The result of stretching to a **Second point of displacement** is shown in drawing **4**.
5. **Copy** drawing **3**.
6. Call **Stretch** and *pick* a crossing-window as shown.

The result of stretching to a **Second point of displacement** is shown in Drawing **6**.

Note

1. A reminder: it may well be that the abbreviations for tools used in this chapter have not been included in the **acad.pgp** file of Releases 12 and 13. It is advisable to call up the **acad.pgp** file in order to check whether the abbreviations have been included.
2. The examples shown in this chapter work just as well in the various releases of AutoCAD LT.
3. In AutoCAD 2000 the prompt sequences will be slightly different to those shown, but all the responses will work just as well. As an example the prompts when **Stretch** is called are:

Command:_stretch
Select objects to stretch by crossing-window or crossing polygon ...
Select objects: c
Specify first corner: *pick* **Specify other corner:** *pick*
Select objects: *right-click*
Specify base point or displacement: *pick*
Specify second point of displacement: *pick*
Command:

Questions

1. What is the recommended method of calling the **Zoom** tool given in this chapter?
2. Why is the **Zoom** tool of importance to all those who operate an AutoCAD system for constructing drawings?
3. What is the difference between **Zoom All** and **Zoom Extents**?
4. When using the **Scale** tool what is the difference between using the **Scale factor** and the **Reference** prompts?
5. When using the **Break** tool why is it important to break in an anticlockwise direction when attempting to break part of a circle?

6. What is the difference between a rectangular array and a polar array?
7. When would it be necessary to *enter* negative numbers when using the **Array** tool?
8. Is it possible to use the **Stretch** tool to change a circle into an ellipse?
9. Have you remembered to check the **acad.pgp** file to ensure that appropriate abbreviations are included in the file?
10. What are the recognised AutoCAD abbreviations for the tools **Scale**, **Array**, **Break** and **Stretch**?

Exercises

1. Figure 7.19: copy the given drawing (without including dimensions) and with the aid of the **Scale** tool reduce it to a scale of 1:2.

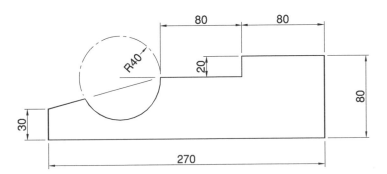

Fig. 7.19 Exercise 1

2. Figure 7.20: copy the upper drawing (without including the dimensions) then, with the aid of the **Stretch** tool, modify the drawing as shown in the lower drawing of Fig. 7.20.
3. Figure 7.21: copy the upper drawing (without including any dimensions) then, with the aid of **Stretch**, modify the drawing to match the lower of the two drawings in Fig. 7.20.
4. Figure 7.22: construct the upper left drawing (without including the dimensions); **Copy** the drawing three times then, with the aid of the **Scale** tool, scale each of the three copies as shown in Fig. 7.22.
5. Figure 7.23: construct the drawing in the top right corner of Fig. 7.23; then, with the **Array** tool, array the drawing 16 times around a central point.
6. Figure 7.24: construct the drawing on the left of the array in Fig. 7.24; then, with the aid of the **Array** tool, complete the array shown in the illustration.

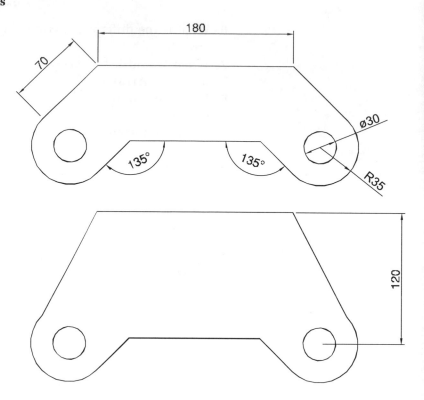

Fig. 7.20 Exercise 2

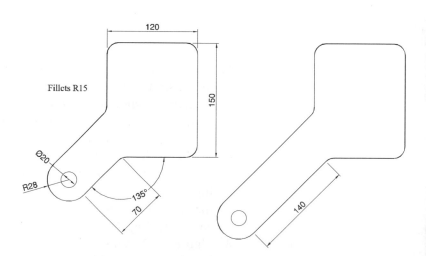

Fig. 7.21 Exercise 3

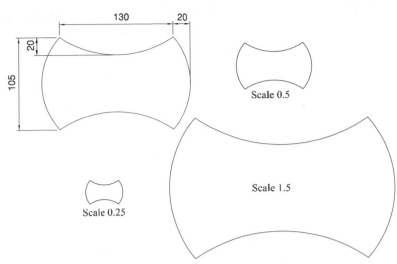

Fig. 7.22 Exercise 4

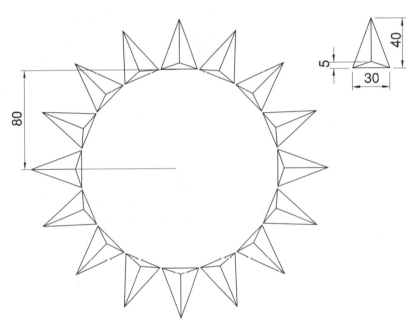

Fig. 7.23 Exercise 5

Fig. 7.24 Exercise 6

7. Figure 7.25: construct the drawing on the left side of Fig. 7.25 and **Array** the outline 24 times around a central point within a circle.

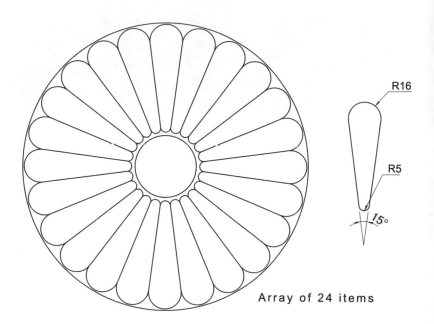

Fig. 7.25 Exercise 7

8. Figure 7.26: construct each of the three smaller drawings in Fig. 7.26; then place them in appropriate positions within a circle of diameter 270, and **Array** them as shown in the illustration.

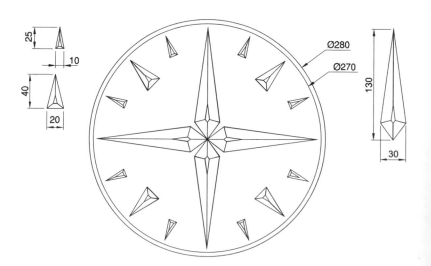

Fig. 7.26 Exercise 8

9. Figure 7.27: construct the array shown in Fig. 7.27 working to the dimensions given within the drawing.

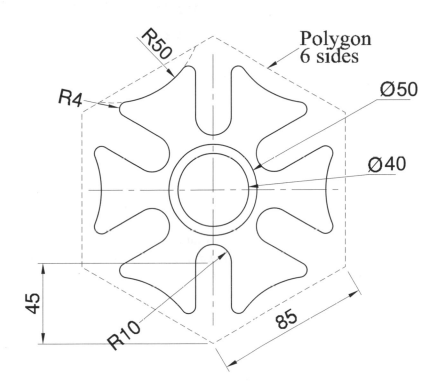

Fig. 7.27 Exercise 9

10. Figure 7.28: construct the array shown in Fig. 7.28 without including any of the dimensions.

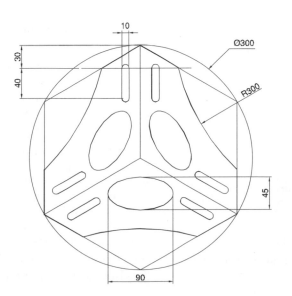

Fig. 7.28 Exercise 10

CHAPTER 8

Fillet, Chamfer, Extend and Explode

Introduction

The four tools described in this chapter can be selected from the Release 12 toolbox or from the **Modify** toolbars of the other releases. However, in Releases 12 and 13 the two tools **Chamfer** and **Fillet** are found in the **Construct** menu whereas in Release 14 and AutoCAD 2000 they are in the **Modify** toolbar. If working in AutoCAD LT 98 (and later releases), the tools can all be found in the **Modify** toolbar or the **Modify** menu.

Remember, if working in either AutoCAD Release 12 or 13, abbreviations for the tools may have to be added to the **acad.pgp** file.

The Chamfer tool

Chamfer
Cha

Release 12
Chamfer icon

Fig. 8.1 Calling the **Chamfer** tool

To call the **Chamfer** tool, *click* on its tool icon in the **Modify** toolbar (toolbox in Release 12), *click* on its name in the **Construct** menu (Releases 12 and 13) or **Modify** menu (Release 14 and AutoCAD 2000), or *enter* **cha** or **chamfer** at the command line (Fig. 8.1).

If using Release 12, the prompt sequences are less complicated than when using later releases of AutoCAD or AutoCAD LT. This does not however prevent the methods shown here from being effectively used.

Chamfer examples (Fig. 8.2)

1. Drawing **1**: with the **Line** tool construct a rectangle of any dimensions.
2. Call **Chamfer**:

Command:_chamfer
(TRIM mode) Current chamfer Dist1 = 10, Dist2 = 10
Polyline/Distance/Angle/Trim/Method/<Select first line>: d

Enter first chamfer distance <10>: 20
Enter second chamfer distance <20>: *right-click*
Command: *right-click* (starts the **Chamfer** sequence again)
(TRIM mode) Current chamfer Dist1 = 10, Dist2 = 10
Polyline/Distance/Angle/Method/<Select first line>: *pick*
Select second line: *pick*
Command:

The chamfer forms (drawing **1** of Fig. 8.2).

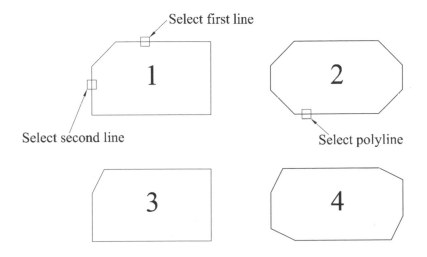

Fig. 8.2 **Chamfer** examples

3. Drawing **2**: with the **Polyline** tool construct a rectangle of any dimensions.
4. Call the **Chamfer** tool:

   Command:_chamfer
   (TRIM mode) Current chamfer Dist1 = 20, Dist2 = 20
   Polyline/Distance/Angle/Trim/Method/<Select first line>: p
   Select 2D polyline: *pick* any line of the polyline
   Command:

   All four corners of the polyline are chamfered (drawing **2** of Fig. 8.2).
5. Drawing **3**: with the **Line** tool construct a rectangle.
6. Call the **Chamfer** tool:

   Command:_chamfer
   (TRIM mode) Current chamfer Dist1 = 10, Dist2 = 10
   Polyline/Distance/Angle/Trim/Method/<Select first line>: d
   Enter first chamfer distance <10>: 20
   Enter second chamfer distance <20>: 10

Command: *right-click* (starts the **Chamfer** sequence again)
(TRIM mode) Current chamfer Dist1 = 20, Dist2 = 10
Polyline/Distance/Angle/Trim/Method/<Select first line>: *pick*
Select second line: *pick*
Command:

The chamfer forms as shown in drawing **3**.
7. Drawing **4**: with the **Polyline** tool construct a rectangle.
8. Keeping **Dist1** as 20 and **Dist2** as 10, use the **Polyline** prompt of **Chamfer** to produce drawing **4**.

Note .

In Release 13 or 14, or AutoCAD 2000, the **Trim** prompt can produce chamfers without trimming of excess lines (see Fig. 8.3). The procedure would be:

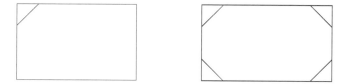

Fig. 8.3 Using the **No Trim** prompt of **Chamfer**

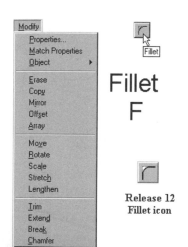

Fig. 8.4 Calling the **Fillet** tool

Command:_chamfer
(TRIM mode) Current chamfer Dist1 = 20, Dist2 = 20
Polyline/Distance/Angle/Trim/Method/<Select first line>: t
Trim/No Trim <Trim>: n (for No Trim)
Polyline/Distance/Angle/Trim/Method/<Select first line>: *pick*
Select second line: *pick*
Command:

With **Dist1** and **Dist2** both set to 20, the line rectangle with a single corner chamfered and the polyline with all corners chamfered will appear as in Fig. 8.3.

The Fillet tool

To call the **Fillet** tool, *click* on its icon in the **Modify** toolbar (toolbox in Release 12), *click* on its name in the **Construct** menu (Releases 12 and 13) or in the **Modify** menu (Release 14 and AutoCAD 2000), or *enter* **f** or **fillet** at the command line (Fig. 8.4).

When using the **Fillet** tool the prompts and responses are very similar to those when using the **Chamfer** tool, apart from the fact that chamfer distances involve two lines and a fillet requires only a radius.

Fillet examples (Fig. 8.5)

1. Drawing **1**: with **Line** draw a rectangle to any dimensions.
2. Call the **Fillet** tool:

Command:_fillet
(TRIM mode) Current fillet radius = 10
Polyline/Radius/Trim/<Select first object>: r
Enter fillet radius <10>: 20
Command: *right-click*
FILLET
(TRIM mode) Current fillet radius = 20
Polyline/Radius/Trim/<Select first object>: *pick*
Select second object: *pick*
Command:

3. Drawing **2**: with **Polyline** draw a rectangle to any dimensions.
4. Call **Fillet**:

Command:_fillet
(TRIM mode) Current fillet radius = 20
Polyline/Radius/Trim/<Select first object>: p
Select 2D polyline: *pick*
Command:

5. Drawing **3**: with **Line** draw a rectangle of any dimensions.

Command:_fillet
(TRIM mode) Current fillet radius = 20
Polyline/Radius/Trim/<Select first object>: t
Trim/No Trim/<Trim>: n
Polyline/Radius/Trim/<Select first object>: *pick*

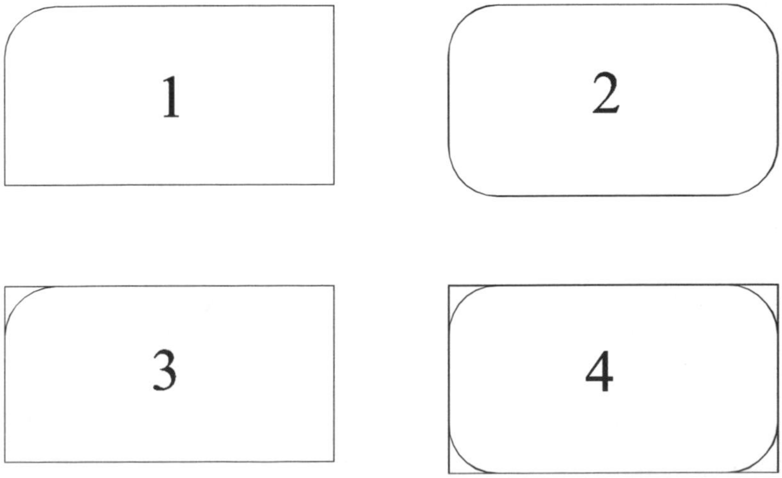

Fig. 8.5 **Fillet** examples

Select second object: *pick*
Command:

6. Drawing **4**: with **Polyline** construct a rectangle to any dimensions.
7. Call **Fillet**:

Command:_fillet
(NOTRIM mode) Current fillet radius = 20
Polyline/Radius/Trim/<Select first object>: p
Select 2D polyline: *pick*
Command:

Fillet examples including circles (Fig. 8.6)

Unlike chamfers, which cannot be formed if one of the objects is a circle or an arc, fillets can be constructed between circles and lines, circles and circles, and arcs and lines. This is shown in the six drawings of Fig. 8.6.

Note

When using either the **Chamfer** or **Fillet** tools, if the chamfer distances are both set to 0 or (in the case of a fillet) the radius is set to 0, crossing lines or lines which do not meeting at a corner will be formed into sharp corners.

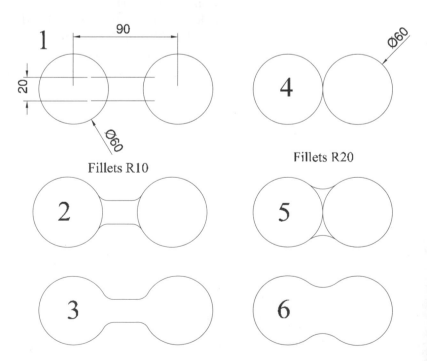

Fig. 8.6 **Fillet** between circles examples

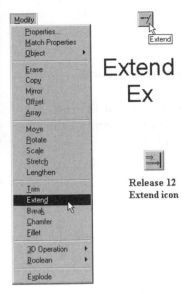

Fig. 8.7 Calling the **Extend** tool

The Extend tool

To call the **Extend** tool, *click* on its icon in the **Modify** toolbar, *click* on its name in the **Modify** menu, or *enter* **ex** or **extend** at the command line (Fig. 8.7).

Note

1. There is some variation in the prompts associated with this tool in the different releases of AutoCAD and AutoCAD LT. The major one is that in Release 12 extensions are only possible from an object to a boundary edge, but in later releases extensions are possible to extended boundary edges.
2. The use of the tool to extend an object to an extended boundary edge is shown in Fig. 8.8 with the prompt sequences from Release 14. Remember however that extending to extended boundary edges is also possible in all releases newer than Release 12.

Extend examples with Release 12 (Fig. 8.8)

1. Drawing **1**: construct a polyline rectangle to any dimensions. Add a line, a polyline (of width 2) and two arcs similar to those shown in Fig. 8.8.

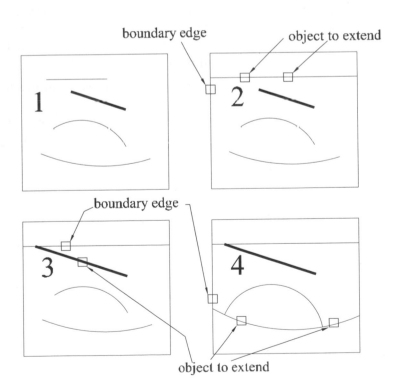

Fig. 8.8 **Extend** examples

2. Call the **Extend** tool:

Command:_extend
Select boundary edge(s) . . .
Select objects: *pick* an edge of the rectangle **1 found**
Select objects: *right-click*
<Select object to extend>/Undo: *pick* one end of the line
<Select object to extend>/Undo: *pick* the other end of the line
<Select object to extend>/Undo: *right-click*
Command:

The result is shown in drawing **2** of Fig. 8.8.
3. Drawing **3**: extend the polyline to the line; the results are shown in drawing **3**.
4. Drawing **4**: extend the lower arc to the rectangle and the other arc to the lower arc; the results are shown in drawing **4**.

Extend examples with Release 14 (Fig. 8.9)

The command line sequence shows as follows:

Command:_extend
Select boundary edges: (Projmode = UCS, Edgemode = No extend)
Select objects: *pick* **1 found**
Select objects: *right-click*
<Select object to extend>/Project/Edge/Undo: e
Extend/No extend <No extend>: e
<Select object to extend>/Project/Edge/Undo: *pick*
Command:

Figure 8.8 shows three examples of the use of the **Extend** prompt.

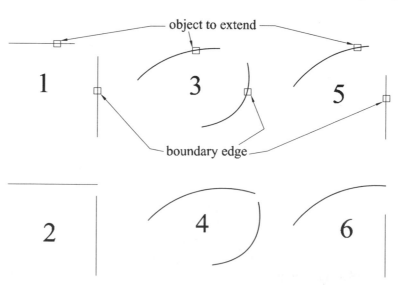

Fig. 8.9 **Extend** examples
(Release 14)

Fig. 8.10 Calling the **Explode** tool

Fig. 8.11 Example 1

The Explode tool

To call the **Explode** tool, *click* on its icon in the **Modify** toolbar, *click* on its name in the **Modify** menu, or *enter* **x** or **explode** at the command line (Fig. 8.10).

Explode: example 1 (Fig. 8.11)

With **Polyline** construct a rectangle of width 6. Call **Explode**:

Command:_explode
Select objects: *pick* **1 found**
Select objects: *right-click*
Command:

The polyline is exploded back to a width of 0.

Explode: example 2 – of a region (Fig. 8.12)

1. Construct a pline rectangle and, centred on its edges, add another polyline rectangle, a circle, a hexagon and an ellipse as shown in the left drawing of Fig. 8.12.

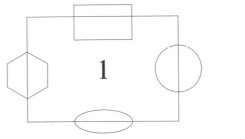

Fig. 8.12 Creating a region

2. Call the **Region** tool, *click* on its icon in the **Draw** toolbar, *click* on its name in the **Draw** menu, or *enter* **reg** or **region** at the command line (Fig. 8.13).

Command:_region
Select objects: *pick* the larger pline rectangle **1 found**
Select objects: *pick* the smaller pline rectangle **1 found**
Select objects: *pick* the circle **1 found**

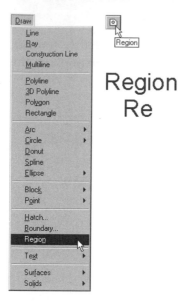

Region
Re

Fig. 8.13 Calling the **Region** tool

Select objects: *pick* the polygon **1 found**
Select objects: *pick* the ellipse **1 found**
Select objects: *right-click*
5 loops extracted
5 regions created
Command:

3. Call the **Boundary** tool (just above **Region** in the **Draw** menu): the **Boundary Creation** dialog box appears.
4. *Click* on the **Make New Boundary Set<** button:

Command:_boundary
Select objects: *pick* the smaller pline rectangle **1 found**
Select objects: *pick* the circle **1 found**
Select objects: *pick* the polygon **1 found**
Select objects: *pick* the ellipse **1 found**
Select objects: *right-click*
Analyzing the selected data ...

5. The **Boundary Creation** dialog box returns. *Click* on the **Pick Points<** button:

Select internal point: *pick* inside the objects on screen
Boundary created 1 polyline
Command:

6. Call the **Move** tool and move the newly created region away from the original set of objects. This newly created region is shown in the right drawing of Fig. 8.9.
7. Now call **Explode** and select the region. When the region has been exploded, you will see that it is made up of individual objects; each object can than be moved away from the region.

Note

The **Explode** tool is of value when inserting blocks (see Chapter 14). There are other situations where **Explode** will be found to be of value, but only its use with regions and blocks will be described in this book.

Questions

1. There are similarities between the prompt sequences of **Chamfer** and **Fillet** – can you describe them?
2. When using AutoCAD Release 13 (and later) there is a **Trim/No trim** prompt in the command line prompt sequences of **Chamfer** and **Fillet** – what is the purpose of these prompts?

3. Can a fillet be drawn between a closed polyline and an arc?
4. Can a fillet be drawn between two arcs?
5. When using AutoCAD Release 13 (and later) objects can be extended to imaginary extensions of other objects – what are the prompt systems for this?
6. When a polyline is acted upon by the **Explode** tool, what happens?

Exercises

1. Construct the polyline outline given in the left drawing of Fig. 8.14. Then, using the **Chamfer** tool set to distances of 10, chamfer the outline as shown in the right drawing.

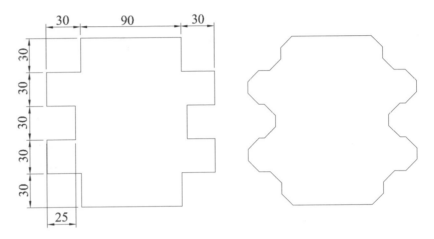

Fig. 8.14 Exercise 1

2. Construct the top left drawing of Fig. 8.15 and from this drawing construct the lower left drawing of the illustration. Construct the upper right drawing of Fig. 8.15. **Copy** the drawing; then, using

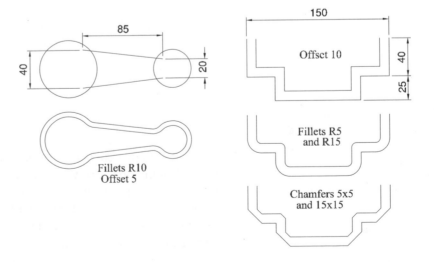

Fig. 8.15 Exercise 2

Fillet set with radius 5, fillet the inner outline, followed by the outer outline with radius set to 15. With the second copy chamfer the inner outline with distances both set to 5 and chamfer the outer outline with distances both set to 15.

3. Construct the left drawing of Fig. 8.16 and with **Fillet** (set to radius first at 30 and then at 10) modify the drawing to produce the right drawing of the illustration.

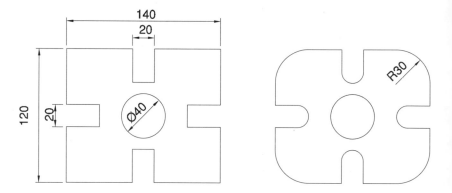

Fig. 8.16 Exercise 3

4. Figure 8.17: construct the left drawing and with **Fillet** set to a radius of 20, modify the drawing to produce the right drawing of the illustration.

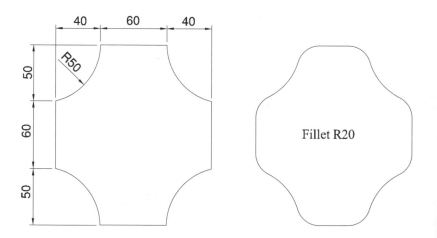

Fig. 8.17 Exercise 4

5. Figure 8.18: construct the upper right drawing of Fig. 8.18 to the given dimensions. **Copy** the drawing; then modify the drawing as shown in the other two drawings on the left. Construct the drawing on the right of Fig. 8.18. **Rotate** the drawing through 90° and use **Fillet** and **Chamfer** to modify the rotated drawing as shown in the lower drawing of Fig. 8.18.

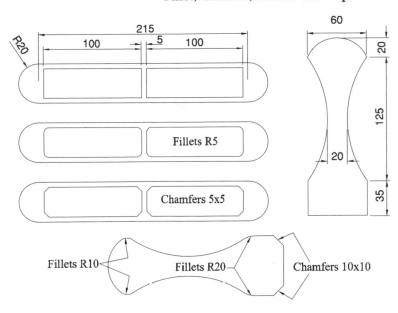

Fig. 8.18 Exercise 5

6. Figure 8.19: construct the upper left drawing of Fig. 8.19, followed by filleting as indicated in the lower left drawing. Then construct the dimensioned vertical drawing, followed by using **Fillet** to produce the right drawing.

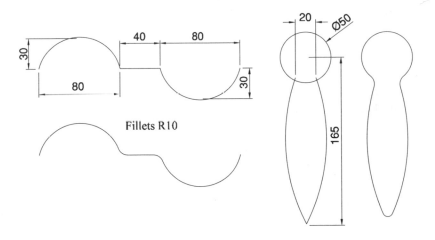

Fig. 8.19 Exercise 6

7. Construct the left drawing of Fig. 8.20 and then modify the drawing as indicated in the right drawing of the illustration.
8. Construct the front view of a pulley wheel illustrated in Fig. 8.21 (do not include dimensions with your drawing).
9. The right drawing of Fig. 8.22 is based upon the construction given in the left drawing. Construct the right drawing of Fig. 8.22 without including the dimensions.

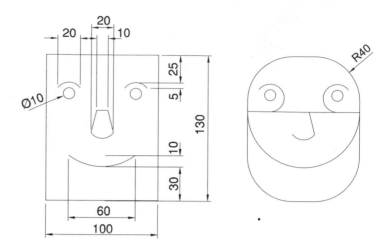

Fig. 8.20 Exercise 7

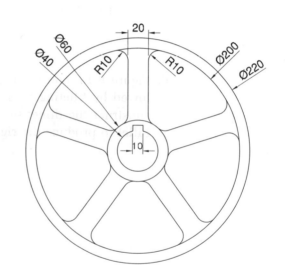

Fig. 8.21 Exercise 8

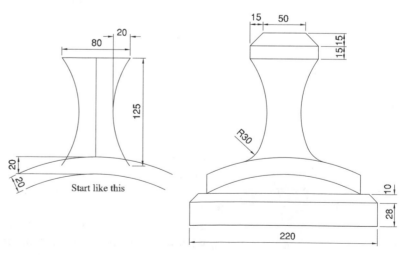

Fig. 8.22 Exercise 9

CHAPTER 9

Hatch and hatching

Introduction

Hatching is the name given to filling selected areas or selected boundary objects with line patterns. Methods of hatching vary between Releases 12 to AutoCAD 2000 and also in AutoCAD LT. In general any of these releases have one common method of hatching from the command line. With Release 12, the only method possible is from the command line. If working with Release 13 or 14 or AutoCAD 2000, LT 98 or LT 2000, hatching is best carried out from the **Boundary Hatch** dialog box. If using AutoCAD 2000, the **Boundary Hatch** dialog box has a significantly different layout to earlier **Boundary Hatch** dialogs, but the methods of including hatch patterns in drawings are much the same as with earlier releases.

In this chapter the general method of placing hatch patterns in drawings from the command line will be described first, followed by the method of using the **Boundary Hatch** dialog box from Release 14, with some details of the amended dialogue box in AutoCAD 2000. If using AutoCAD LT, the methods described are equally valid.

Hatching from the command line

Although the prompt sequences vary slightly between releases, in general the method described in Example 1 can be used in all the releases.

Hatch example 1: command line (Fig. 9.2)

1. Drawing **1**: construct a rectangle with the **Line** tool to any dimensions
2. At the command line:

   Command: *enter* hatch
   Pattern (? or name/U,style)<ANSI31>: *enter* ?
   Pattern(s) to list <*>: *right-click*

An **AutoCAD Text Window** appears listing names of the available hatch patterns with details of what the patterns represent (Fig. 9.1). Choose a suitable pattern, then close the window by *clicking* on its **Close** button.

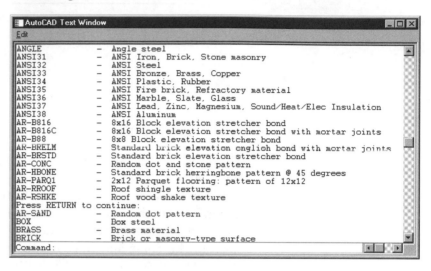

Fig. 9.1 **AutoCAD Text Window** showing names of hatch patterns

3. After choosing the hatch pattern:

Command: hatch
Pattern (? or name/U,style)<ANSI31>: *enter* AR-BRELM
Scale of pattern <1.000>: 3
Angle for pattern <0>: *right-click*
Select objects: *pick* each line of the rectangle in turn **4 found**
Select objects: *right-click*

The rectangle is hatched (Fig. 9.2, drawing **2**).

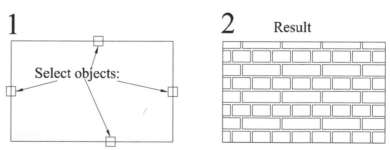

Fig. 9.2 Example 1

The Hatch tool

To call the **Hatch** tool in all but Release 12, either *click* on its icon in the **Draw** toolbar, *click* on **Hatch . . .** in the **Draw** menu, or *enter* **bh** or **bhatch** at the command line (Fig. 9.3). Note: do not *enter* **hatch** in order to use the **Boundary Hatch** dialog.

Fig. 9.3 Calling the **Bhatch** tool

Hatch example 2: Releases 13 or 14 (Fig. 9.4)

1. Construct the top left drawing of Fig. 9.4 to any size.
2. Call the **Hatch** tool: the **Boundary Hatch** dialog box appears. In the dialog box, select the hatch pattern **ANSI31** and *enter* **2** in the **Scale** box.
3. In the dialog box *click* on the **Pick Points<** button: the dialog box disappears.
4. In the drawing *pick* within the areas you want to carry the hatch pattern (the dialog box reappears).
5. In the dialog box *click* on the **Preview Hatch<** button: the dialog box disappears. The drawing shows the hatch pattern in the

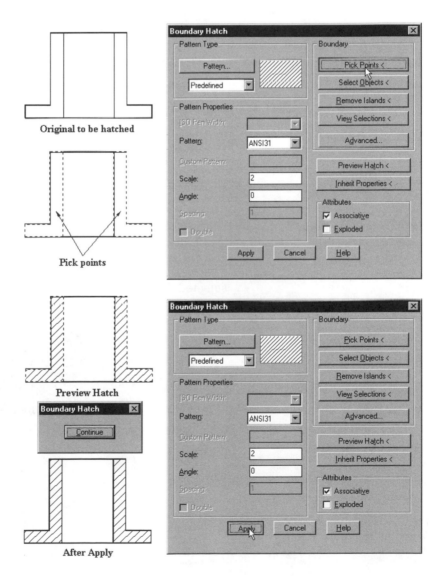

Fig. 9.4 Example 2 (Releases 13 and 14)

areas previously *picked*, together with a box with **Continue**. *Click* on the **Continue** button (the dialog box reappears).

6. If satisfied with the hatching, *click* on the **Apply** button: the dialog disappears and the drawing displays with the hatching in place.

7. If not satisfied with the hatching, the **Pattern**, **Scale** or **Angle** can be changed and another attempt at previewing made.

Notes

1. In Release 14 the **Boundary Hatch** dialog box contains a **Pattern** button. *Clicking* on this button brings up **Hatch pattern palettes**, from which patterns can be selected. The first of these palettes is shown in Fig. 9.5.

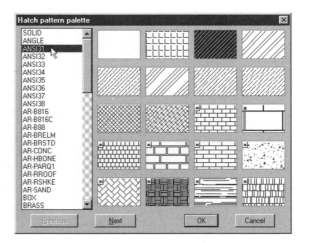

Fig. 9.5 **Hatch pattern palette** (Release 14)

2. These palettes are not available in Release 13. Patterns can be selected from a popup list available by *left-clicking* in the **Pattern** box. The first part of this popup list is shown in Fig. 9.6.

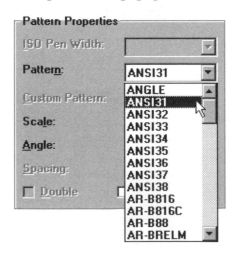

Fig. 9.6 Selecting a pattern from the **Boundary Hatch** dialog box (Release 13)

Hatch example 3: AutoCAD 2000 (Fig. 9.7)

1. Construct the top left drawing in Fig. 9.7 to any size.
2. Call the **Hatch** tool: the **Boundary Hatch** dialog box appears. *Click* in the **Swatch** box. The **Hatch Pattern Palette** dialog appears. *Double-click* on the **ANSI31** pattern in the **ISO** palette: the **ANSI** pattern now appears in the **Swatch** box.
3. *Enter* **2** in the **Scale** box and *click* on the **Pick Points<** button. The dialog box disappears. *Click* within areas of the drawing where hatching is to be placed.

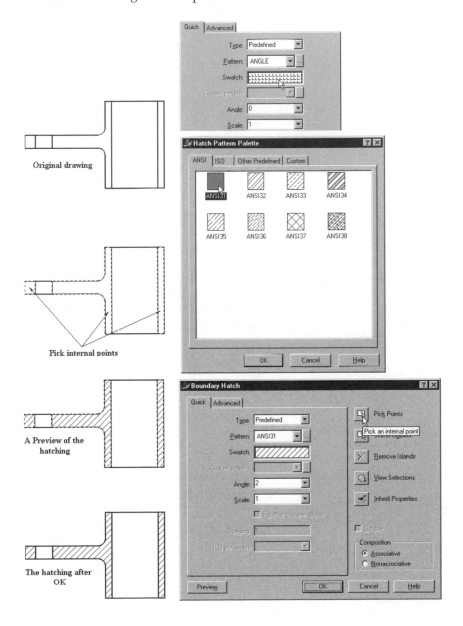

Original drawing

Pick internal points

A Preview of the
hatching

The hatching after
OK

Fig. 9.7 **Hatch** example
(AutoCAD 2000)

4. *Right-click* and a menu appears: *left-click* on **Preview**, followed by a *right-click* which redisplays the dialog box. If satisfied with the hatching *click* on the **OK** button of the dialog box.

Notes

1. Although the method of hatching through the **Boundary Hatch** dialog box appears rather complicated, once you have used the system several times it becomes much quicker.
2. Despite the differences between the **Boundary Hatch** dialog boxes of Releases 13 and 14, and AutoCAD 2000, in effect the methods of hatching are very similar.
3. There are occasions when you may prefer to apply hatching from the command line (you will need to know the name of the hatch pattern).
4. In the above examples using the **Boundary Hatch** dialog box, the method of picking points has been employed. The dialog boxes include a button **Select Objects**. It is sometimes an advantage to be able to *pick* the objects surrounding an area to be hatched. Each object surrounding the area is *picked* in turn when this method is used.

Some more examples of hatching

Example of basic hatching (Fig. 9.8)

Figure 9.8 shows a front view of a house using three hatch patterns. The brickwork is hatched with the pattern **BRICK**, the roof is hatched with the pattern **ANGLE**, and corners of walls are hatched with the pattern **AR-CONC**.

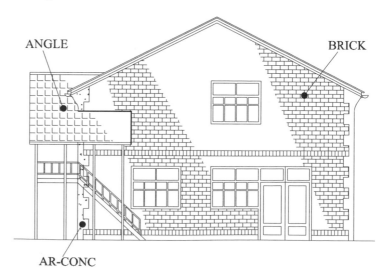

Fig. 9.8 Example 1

Examples of section hatching (Figs 9.9 and 9.10)

The hatching of sectional views forms an important part of many technical drawings. Figures 9.9 and 9.10 show examples of different forms of hatching.

Figure 9.9 shows a front view of a component with two plan views. The plans are in sectional view, that on the left is 'half section'; because of the symmetry of the component, forming a section in one half of the plane is quite sufficient to show the complete shape and the internal parts. The right-hand plan is a full sectional view. It is common when constructing sectional views in engineering drawings to use the hatch pattern **ANSI31** as the pattern of choice.

Figure 9.10 shows a sectional front view through a bracket in which a screw is included in a hole. This sectional view shows

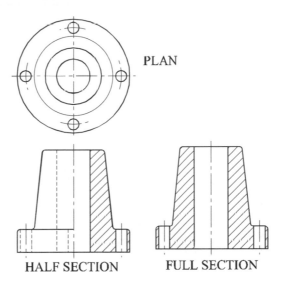

PLAN

HALF SECTION   FULL SECTION

Fig. 9.9 Section hatch examples

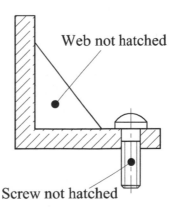

Web not hatched

Screw not hatched

Fig. 9.10 Section hatch example

examples of rules which are commonly applied to hatchings which contain features such as webs, ribs, screws, bolts and other similar parts. Such parts are shown in outside views within the sectional view. In this example the web and the screw are shown in outside views (i.e. they are not hatched).

Examples of hatching with a variety of patterns (Fig. 9.11)

Figure 9.11 shows four outlines which have been hatched with different patterns. The outlines are the same length and width but have differently shaped corners. The scale and angle of the patterns within the outlines vary according to the chosen pattern.

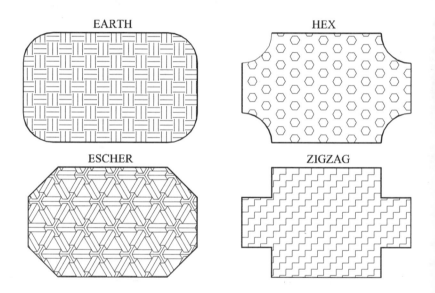

Fig. 9.11 Hatching in a variety of patterns

Associative hatching

The **Boundary Hatch** dialog boxes of Release 13 or 14, and AutoCAD 2000, include a check box (or a radio button) labelled **Associative**. If a tick (or a dot) shows in the check box (or radio button) hatched areas within hatched areas can be moved and the hatch pattern of the larger area accommodates this movement. Figure 9.12 shows the **Hatch Boundary** dialog box of Release 14 and although the dialog boxes of Release 13 and of AutoCAD 2000 are slightly different, the **Associative** option is available in both releases. Note: this facility is not available when working with Release 12.

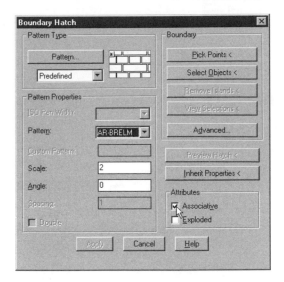

Fig. 9.12 **Boundary Hatch** dialog box (Release 14) showing the **Associative** checkbox

Example of associative hatching (Fig. 9.13)

1. Call the **Hatch** tool: in the **Boundary Hatch** dialog box, ensure that the **Associative** option is selected.
2. Construct drawing **1** of Fig. 9.13, using the hatch pattern **AR_BRELM**.
3. Call the **Move** tool: 'window' the smaller unhatched double rectangle and move it to another position. The surrounding hatch pattern accommodates this movement.

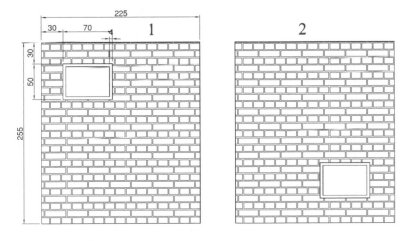

Fig. 9.13 **Associative hatching** example

Advanced hatching options

Taking the **Boundary Hatch** dialog box of Release 13 as an example, Fig. 9.14 shows the **Style** part of the **Advanced Options** dialog box,

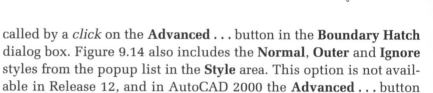

Fig. 9.14 **Advanced Options**
dialog box (Release 13)

called by a *click* on the **Advanced . . .** button in the **Boundary Hatch**
dialog box. Figure 9.14 also includes the **Normal**, **Outer** and **Ignore**
styles from the popup list in the **Style** area. This option is not available in Release 12, and in AutoCAD 2000 the **Advanced . . .** button
is replaced by a tab.

Example of hatching using advanced options (Fig. 9.15)

1. Drawing **1**: construct a pline rectangle 230 × 130, with **Fillets**
   R25; **Offset** the rectangle by 30.

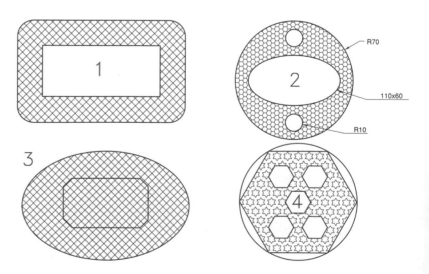

Fig. 9.15 **Hatch** examples:
advanced options

2. Call **Bhatch** and *click* on the **Advanced** button. In the **Style** popup list, ensure that the **Style** is set to **Normal**.
3. Select the pattern **AR-HBONE**.
4. *Click* on the **Pick Points<** button and *pick a* point between the outer outline and the rectangle. Apply the pattern as in drawing **1**.
5. Drawing **2**: construct the drawing as shown.
6. Reset the **Advanced Style** to **Outer** and hatch drawing **2** with the pattern **HONEY**.
7. Drawing **3**: construct an ellipse 200 × 130 and within the ellipse construct a central rectangle 100 × 60 and **Chamfer** to 10.
8. Reset the **Advanced Style** to **Ignore** and hatch the drawing with the pattern **NET3**.
9. Drawing **4**: construct hexagons as shown, inscribed within circles – outer of radius 70, others of radius 15.
10. Reset **Style** to **Normal** and hatch the drawing with the pattern **STARS**.

Questions

1. What happens when **hatch** is *entered* at the command line?
2. How can you find which material a hatch pattern represents?
3. What is the difference between the picking points and picking objects methods of selecting hatch boundaries?
4. If you are dissatisfied with a resulting hatching after using the **Preview** button, how can the hatching be amended?
5. Can you explain the differences between the three styles of advanced hatching?
6. In the first example of hatching given in Fig. 9.8 can you explain how the **BRICK** pattern hatching was placed in two separate areas?
7. There is a possible error in the left drawing of Fig. 9.9, in that it is not necessary to show hidden detail in the left part of a half section. Why is this so?
8. When **hatch** is *entered* at the command line and the response is **u**, what should you expect to do? Note that this is not covered in this chapter, but some experimentation is good practice when learning how to work in AutoCAD.
9. What is associative hatching?
10. What is the abbreviation for the **Hatch** tool if *entering* abbreviations from the command line (rather than selecting the tool from a toolbar or menu)?

Exercises

1. Construct the four outlines shown in Fig. 9.16 as indicated by drawings **1–4**, then hatch as follows: drawing **1** – inner hatching **AR-HBONE**, middle hatching **ESCHER**, outer hatching **DOTS**; drawing **2** – hatching **HONEY**; drawing **3** – hatching ellipse **EARTH**; hatching circles **NET3**; drawing **4** – hatchings **HOUND** and **Dash**.

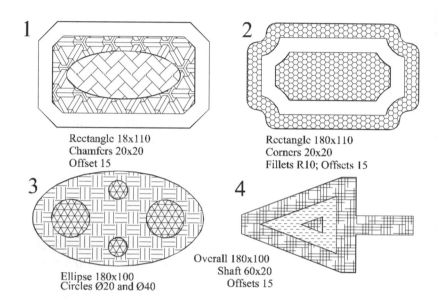

Rectangle 18x110
Chamfers 20x20
Offset 15

Rectangle 180x110
Corners 20x20
Fillets R10; Offsets 15

Ellipse 180x100
Circles Ø20 and Ø40

Overall 180x100
Shaft 60x20
Offsets 15

Fig. 9.16 Exercise 1

2. Figure 9.17: construct drawing **1** as shown. Hatch the drawing as shown in drawing **2**. Construct drawing **3** as shown and hatch as indicated. In both hatchings the pattern is **ANSI31**.

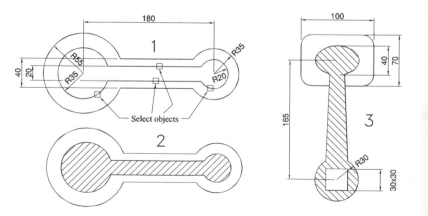

Fig. 9.17 Exercise 2

3. Figure 9.18: construct drawing **1** and multiple copy three times. Then hatch each of the four drawings as shown. The patterns are **AR-HBONE** and **EARTH**.

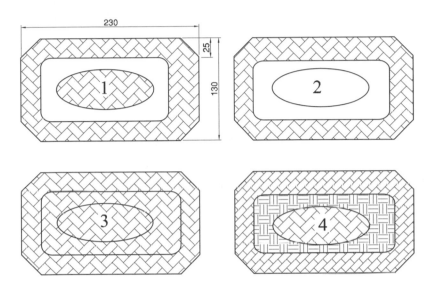

Fig. 9.18 Exercise 3

4. Figure 9.19: a pictorial view of a sectional view through the centre of a tool gauge is shown, together with a two-view orthographic projection of the tool. Construct the right-hand view of the orthographic projection and replace the left-hand view with a sectional view based upon the pictorial drawing.

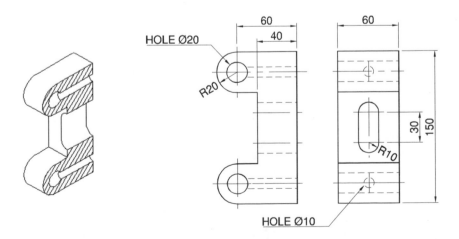

Fig. 9.19 Exercise 4

5. Figure 9.20: a front view and a plan of a support stand are shown, together with a pictorial view of the stand. Copy the upper of the two views and instead of the lower view construct a sectional view with the cutting plane passing through the centre of the upper view.

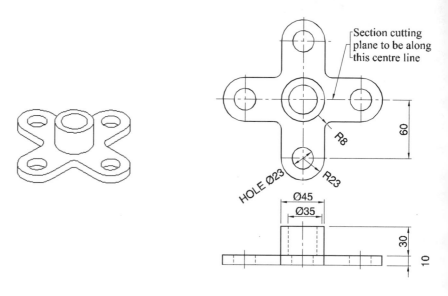

Fig. 9.20 Exercise 5

Note

See Chapters 12 and 11 concerning orthographic projection and dimensioning.

CHAPTER 10

Text

Introduction

Before being able to add text in a drawing on screen, the text style (font) to be used, together with its size and other parameters, must first be chosen in the **Text Style** dialog box. This box varies between AutoCAD releases, and in Release 12 is named **Select Text Font**. Figure 10.1 shows the methods employed in the different releases to call the dialog box.

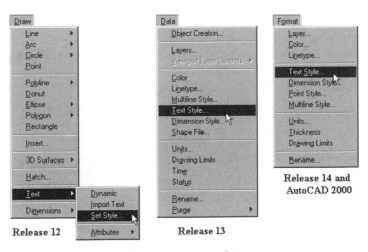

Fig. 10.1 Calling the **Text Style** dialog box

The default text fonts held in AutoCAD are shown in Fig. 10.2. In general there are two types of fonts: AutoCAD fonts and Windows' TrueType fonts. Figure 10.2 shows all the fonts commonly held in AutoCAD. In this illustration the fonts with a 'TT' icon preceding the name are TrueType and those preceded by an icon in the form of a pair of callipers are AutoCAD SHX fonts.

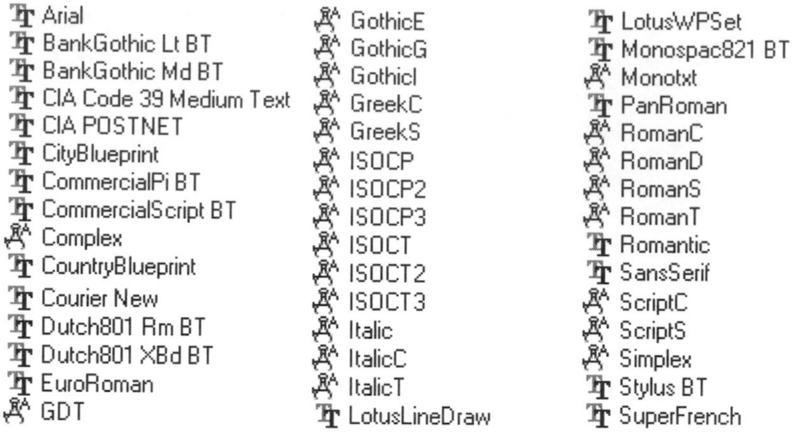

Arial
BankGothic Lt BT
BankGothic Md BT
CIA Code 39 Medium Text
CIA POSTNET
CityBlueprint
CommercialPi BT
CommercialScript BT
Complex
CountryBlueprint
Courier New
Dutch801 Rm BT
Dutch801 XBd BT
EuroRoman
GDT
GothicE
GothicG
GothicI
GreekC
GreekS
ISOCP
ISOCP2
ISOCP3
ISOCT
ISOCT2
ISOCT3
Italic
ItalicC
ItalicT
LotusLineDraw
LotusWPSet
Monospac821 BT
Monotxt
PanRoman
RomanC
RomanD
RomanS
RomanT
Romantic
SansSerif
ScriptC
ScriptS
Simplex
Stylus BT
SuperFrench

Fig. 10.2 Text fonts generally available in AutoCAD

Setting text styles

The methods shown here are those employed in AutoCAD Release 14, but despite differences in the dialog boxes between releases, similar methods can be employed in the other releases.

Example: setting text styles

1. Call **Style**: the **Text Style** dialog box appears (Fig. 10.3).

Text Style
Style Name
ARIAL
New...
Rename...
Delete
Apply
Close
Help
Font
Font Name:
Arial
Arial Black
BankGothic Lt BT
BankGothic Md BT
CIA Code 39 Medium Text
CIA POSTNET
Font Style:
Regular
Italic
Bold
Bold Italic
Height:
10
Use Big Font
Effects
Upside down
Backwards
Vertical
Width Factor:
1
Oblique Angle:
0
Preview
AaBbCcD
Preview

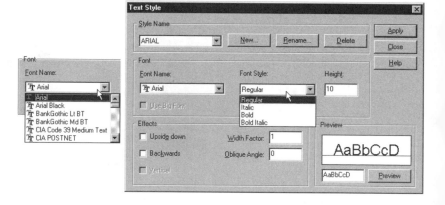

Fig. 10.3 **Text Style** dialog box (Release 14)

2. *Click* on the **New** button: the **New Text Style** dialog box appears showing **style1** in the **Style Name:** box (Fig. 10.4). *Click* on the **OK** button. The name **STYLE1** appears in the **Style Name** box.

New Text Style
Style Name:
style1
OK
Cancel

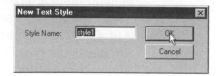

Fig. 10.4 **New Style Name** dialog box

Fig. 10.5 Popup **Font name** list

Fig. 10.6 **Rename Text Style** dialog box

Fig. 10.7 Popup **Style Name** list

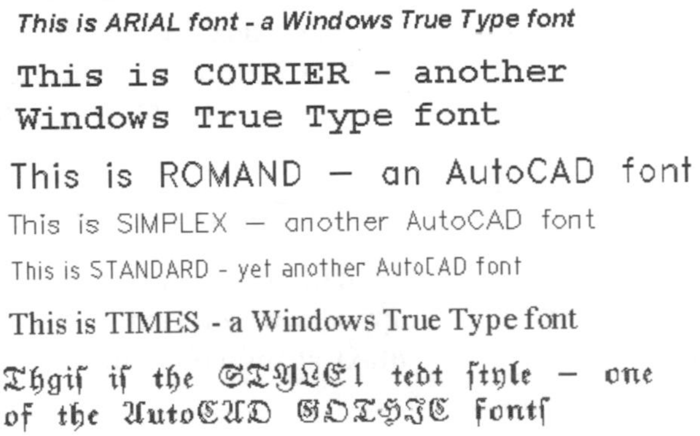

Fig. 10.8 Some text styles from any of the releases of AutoCAD

3. *Click* in the **Font Name** box and choose the name **Arial** from the popup list (Fig. 10.5).
4. *Click* on the **Rename . . .** button and then, in the **Rename Text Style** dialogue box which then appears, *enter* **Arial** over the name **Style1** (Fig. 10.6).

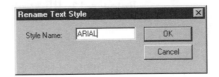

5. Repeat items 2–4 with a number of new styles. Figure 10.7 shows the results of forming seven new styles. Figure 10.8 gives examples of the text associated with these chosen text styles.

This is ARIAL font - a Windows True Type font

This is COURIER - another Windows True Type font

This is ROMAND — an AutoCAD font

This is SIMPLEX — another AutoCAD font

This is STANDARD - yet another AutoCAD font

This is TIMES - a Windows True Type font

This is the STYLE1 text style — one of the AutoCAD GOTHIC fonts

Note

1. Each new style needs its **Height**, **Width Factor** (usually 1) and **Oblique Angle** (usually 0) *entered* when the style is renamed. Note the other two parameters **Upside down** and **Backwards** which can be set by *clicking* in their check boxes.
2. When text is to be *entered* in a drawing, the desired text style is selected from the **Style Name** popup list (its height and other parameters can be changed if necessary).
3. Windows' TrueType fonts can generally be *entered* into a drawing in regular, italic, bold or bold italic forms; AutoCAD fonts cannot.
4. The methods of setting text styles and the given examples are the same in AutoCAD LT 98 and LT 2000.

Adding text to drawings

In general, there are two methods by which text can be added to drawings. The first is **dtext** (dynamic text) which is common to Releases 12–14 and AutoCAD 2000. The second is **mtext** (multiline text) which is available in Releases 13 and 14, AutoCAD 2000 and AutoCAD LT (98 and 2000), although the text editor is different in Release 13. Illustrations in this chapter are from Release 14.

Note

1. If using either Release 12 or 13 it may be necessary to include the abbreviations for the tools **dtext** and **mtext** into your **acad.pgp** file.
2. When using the **dtext** tool, when text is *entered* from the keyboard at the command line it immediately appears in the AutoCAD (or AutoCAD LT) window. Hence its name 'dynamic' text.
3. When using the **mtext** tool, text is *entered* into the **Edit MText** dialog box (when working in Release 13) or into the **Multiline Text Editor** when working in Release 14, AutoCAD 2000, and AutoCAD LT 98 and 2000.

The Dtext and Mtext tools

To call the tool, *click* on **Single Line Text** in the sub-menu that appears when **Text** is *selected* from the **Draw** menu, or *enter* **dt** or **dtext** at the command line (Fig. 10.9).

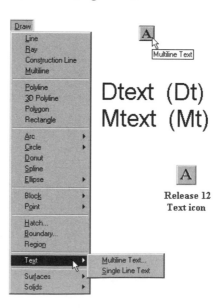

Fig. 10.9 Calling the **Dtext** and **Mtext** tools

Example: Dtext

1. Select the required text style in the **Text Style** dialog box. Select the style **TIMES** from the style name popup list.
2. Call **Dtext**:

   Command: *enter* dt *right-click*
   Justify/Style/<Start point>: *enter* This is how dtext appears as it is entered into the command line *right-click* (as the text is typed it appears on screen)
   Text: *right-click*
   Command:

3. If another line of text is to be added, *enter* it at the second **Text:** prompt. As many lines of text as you wish can be placed on screen using this method.

   Note

When adding text using the **Dtext** tool, the following %% calls can be used to place the degree symbol (°), the diameter symbol (Ø), the tolerance symbol (±) and the percent symbol (%) symbol:

Enter **45%%d** – the result will be **45°**
Enter **%%c60** – the result will be **Ø60**
Enter **100%%p0.5** – the result will be **100±0.5**
Enter **50%%%** – the result will be **50%**

Example: Mtext (Fig. 10.10)

This example is taken from AutoCAD LT 2000, but could equally be taken from Release 14 or AutoCAD 2000. It is also applicable to Release 13, but with a different dialog box (**Edit MText**).

Select the **Arial** font (a TrueType font) from the **Text Style** dialogue box. Set its height to 12 and **Bold**. Call **Mtext**:

Command:_mtext Current text style "ARIAL" Height: 12
Specify first corner: *pick*
Specify opposite corner or [Height/Justify/Line spacing/Rotation/ Style/Width]: *pick* (Fig. 10.10 shows how the window in which text will be placed appears when the two corners have been *picked*).

The **Multiline Text Editor** appears. *Enter* the desired text in the text window of the editor (central part of Fig. 10.10) and *left-click* on the **OK** button. The text appears on screen within the area defined by the box *picked* in response to the **first** and **opposite** corner prompts (lower part of Fig. 10.10).

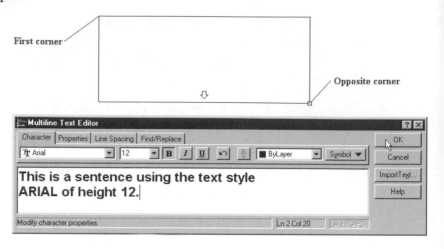

Fig. 10.10 **Mtext** example

> This is a sentence using the text style
> ARIAL of height 12.

Note

The prompts shown in this example are different from those which appear in Releases 12, 13 and 14. However their meanings are much the same. Commencing with AutoCAD 2000 (and LT 2000) a more expressive method of prompt lines has been introduced, such as those shown in this example.

Example: editing text (Fig. 10.12)

Text can be edited in the **Edit Text** dialog box. The box is called to screen by *entering* **ddedit** in all releases of AutoCAD or AutoCAD LT, or by calling the **Edit Text** tool in Release 13 or 14, and in AutoCAD 2000 (also AutoCAD LT 98 and LT 2000). Figure 10.11 shows methods of calling the tool (except in Release 12): *click* on **Text . . .** in the **Object** sub-menu of the **Modify** toolbar, or *click* on the **Edit Text** icon in the **Modify II** toolbar (Release 14, LT 98 and LT 2000).

1. Call **Edit Text**:

   Command:_ddedit
   <Select an annotation object>/Undo: *pick* the line of text to be edited

2. The **Edit Text** dialog box appears. Edit the text as if working in a word processor. When completed, *left-click* on the **OK** button:

   <Select an annotation object>/Undo: *right-click*
   Command:

Fig. 10.11 Calling the **Edit Text** tool

Release 14, LT 98 and
AutoCAD and LT 2000

3. The edited text appears in place of the original text as shown in the bottom lines of Fig. 10.12.

Text before editing   This is ROMAND style text
and itt is 12 unuts hight

Text after editing   This is ROMAND style text
and it is 12 units high

Fig. 10.12 **Edit Text** example

Example: the Spell tool (Fig. 10.14)

The **Spell** tool works in a different manner to the **Edit Text** tool (the **Spell** tool is not available in Release 12). To call the tool, *click* on **Spelling** in the **Tools** menu, or *enter* **sp** or **spell** at the command line (Fig. 10.13).

1. Call the **Spell** tool (Fig. 10.13):

   Command:_spell
   Select objects: *pick* the line of text to be edited **1 found**
   Select objects: *right-click*

2. The **Check Spelling** dialog box appears. Badly spelt words appear in the **Current word** area, with alternatives in the **Suggestions:** window. The complete line of text being edited appears in the **Context** area of the dialog box.

Fig. 10.13 Calling the **Spell** tool

3. Using the **Change** or **Ignore** buttons, the text can be edited.
4. When completed an **AutoCAD Message** box appears with the phrase **Spelling check complete**. If satisfied *click* the **OK** button.

Fig. 10.14 **Spell** example

Questions

1. What are the differences between **Dtext** and **Mtext**?
2. There are two types of fonts available in AutoCAD; can you name them?
3. Of the two types which type can be placed on screen in bold, italic, or bold italic styles?

4. Have you experimented with the various editing methods available in the **Multiline Text Editor**?
5. There are two methods of editing the spelling when working in AutoCAD; can you describe them?
6. When using the **Dtext** tool, how can the °, Ø, ± and % symbols be included with text?
7. If using the **Mtext** tool it is not necessary to use the methods from question **6**. Why is this so? How are the symbols included with text when working with **Mtext**?

Exercises

1. Load your AutoCAD drawing template. Open the **Text Style** dialog box and set up a number of text styles as described on page 126. Save your drawing template which will now include these text styles.
2. *Enter* some misspelt text on screen. Call the **Edit Text** dialog box to screen and edit the bad spelling in the text.
3. Add further misspelt text on screen and edit it using the **Spell** tool.
4. Add the following examples of text on screen using the **Dtext** tool: **120±0.005; 45°; Ø60 mm**.
5. Repeat exercise 4 using the **Mtext** tool.

CHAPTER 11

Dimensioning

Introduction

Before being able to add dimensions to drawings, the style of dimensions needs to be either selected (if previously set) or set up in the **Dimension Styles** dialog box (in AutoCAD 2000 this is called the **Dimension Style Manager**). Although the dialog box and its associated sub-dialogs are different from release to release, the methods of setting up a dimension style are inherently similar. Once a dimension style has been set up, there are, in general, two methods by which dimensions can be added to a drawing: by *picking* dimension tools from **Dimensions** toolbars, or by *entering* abbreviations and dimensions at the command line.

Dimension styles

The example of setting up a dimension style shown here uses Release 14, with some reference to AutoCAD 2000 and AutoCAD LT 2000.

Example: setting up a new dimension style

No matter which release is in use *entering* **ddim** at the command line brings up the relevant dimension style dialog box; this is the method shown here.

1. Set up **ROMAND** as the current text style with a height of 5 (see page 126).
2. At the command line:

Command: *enter* ddim

The **Dimension Style** dialog box appears (Fig. 11.1). Note the three buttons **Geometry . . .**, **Format . . .** and **Annotation**. *Clicking* on any one brings up a dialog box. Settings need to be made in each of these three sub-dialogs to complete the setting of a dimension style.

Fig. 11.1 **Dimension Styles** dailog box (Release 14)

3. *Click* on the **Geometry . . .** button: the **Geometry** dialog box appears. Make settings as shown in Fig. 11.2, then *click* on the **OK** button.

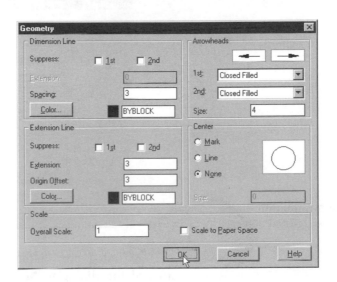

Fig. 11.2 **Geometry** dialog box with suggested settings

4. The **Dimension Styles** dialog reappears. *Click* on the **Format . . .** button and in the **Format** dialog box which appears make setting as shown in Fig. 11.3. Then *click* the **OK** button of the dialog box; the **Dimension Styles** dialog box reappears.
5. *Click* the **Annotation** button and in the **Annotation** dialog box which appears make settings as shown in Fig. 11.4.
6. While still in the **Annotation** dialog, *click* on the **Units . . .** button in the **Primary Units** area of the dialogue and set **Precision** to **0**. Although it does not matter at this stage it is as well to set the **Tolerance** units to **0** at the same time. *Click* on the **OK** buttons of both the **Primary Units** and of the **Annotation** dialog boxes. The **Dimension Styles** dialog box reappears.

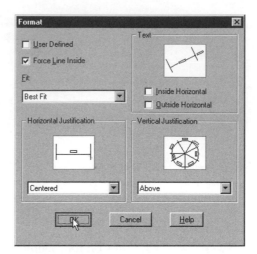

Fig. 11.3 **Format** dialog box
with suggested settings

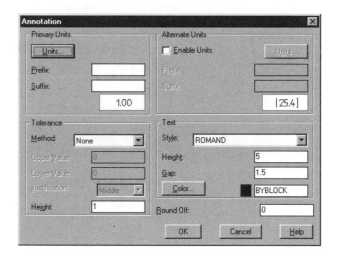

Fig. 11.4 **Annotation** dialog
box with suggested settings

7. In the dialog box change the **Name** in the **Dimension Style** area of the dialog to **MY_NAME**, followed by *clicking* the **OK** button.

8. The dimension style has been completed. It is suggested you re-save the settings in your drawing template for future use.

Example: the Dimension Style Manager

When working in AutoCAD 2000 or AutoCAD LT 2000, dimensions styles are set in the **Dimension Style Manager** (Fig. 11.5). Although the appearance of this dialog box is different from earlier dimension style dialogs, the method of setting up dimension styles is very similar. One major difference, however, is the very useful **Preview** box in the dialog box. *Clicking* on the **Modify . . .** button of the dialog brings up the group of **Modify Dimension Style** dialogs.

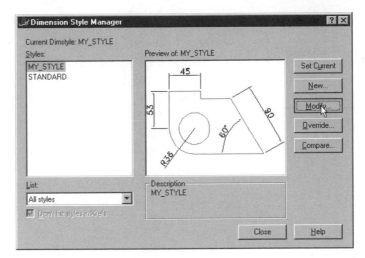

Fig. 11.5 **Dimension Style Manager** (AutoCAD 2000 and AutoCAD LT 2000)

In all there are six dialog boxes, selected from the tabs at the top of the **Modify Dimension Style** dialog box (Fig. 11.6).

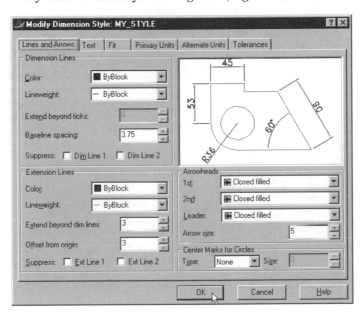

Fig. 11.6 **Modify Dimensions Style** dialog boxes

Adding dimensions to a drawing

As mentioned, there are two main methods of adding dimensions to a drawing: either by *picking* a dimension tool from a toolbar or by *entering* abbreviations and figures at the command line. Throughout AutoCAD's development, dimensioning has been under constant review and has received many additions and improvements. This is hardly surprising when one considers how important dimensioning is in technical drawings.

Example: dimensioning with tools from toolbars

Figure 11.7 shows the tool icons and toolbars from the various releases of AutoCAD. Figure 11.8 is the **Dimension** toolbar from Release 14. Despite the changes which have been made to the toolbars, the details of tool icons and tool names have changed little between Release 13 and AutoCAD 2000 (and AutoCAD LT 2000). This means that the toolbar and tool names given in Fig. 11.8 are reasonably representative of the tools in all releases other than Release 12.

Note that to call the dimension tools at the command line the abbreviation **dim** is common to all releases of AutoCAD and AutoCAD LT.

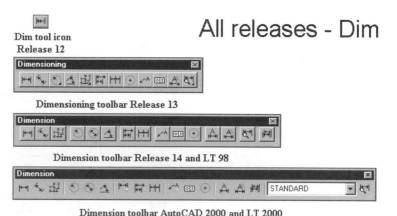

Fig. 11.7 **Dimension** tool icons and toolbars (Releases 12–14 and AutoCAD 2000)

Dimensioning toolbar Release 13

Dimension toolbar Release 14 and LT 98

Dimension toolbar AutoCAD 2000 and LT 2000

Fig. 11.8 The **Dimension** tools in a typical toolbar

Examples of dimensioning using the toolbar

The examples are taken from Releases 13 and 14, and AutoCAD 2000, LT 97, LT 98 and LT 2000. Only a limited selection of tools from the toolbar are shown in these examples. (Release 12 does not include a **Dimension** toolbar.)

Example 1: linear dimensions (Fig. 11.9)

1. *Click* on the **Linear Dimension** tool icon in the **Dimension** toolbar.
2. The command line will show:

   Command:_dimlinear
   First extension line origin or press ENTER to select: *pick*
   Second extension line origin: *pick*
   Dimension line location: *pick*
   Dimension text = 170
   Command:

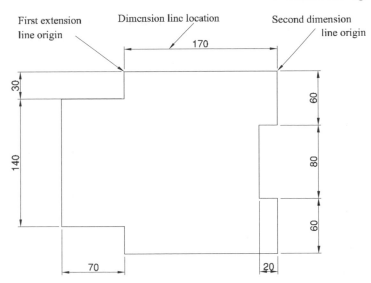

Fig. 11.9 Linear dimension example

3. *Right-click* to add the other dimensions as shown in Fig. 11.9. It does not matter whether the dimensions are horizontal or vertical, the dimensions automatically adjust.
4. Continue adding linear dimensions until the whole drawing is dimensioned.

Example 2: aligned dimensions (Fig. 11.10)

1. Construct a drawing similar to that shown in Fig. 11.10.
2. *Pick* the **Aligned Dimension** tool in the **Dimension** toolbar:

Command:_dimaligned
First extension line origin or press ENTER to select: *pick*
Second extension line origin: *pick*

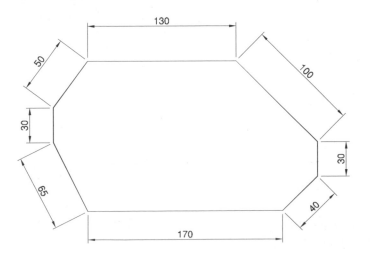

Fig. 11.10 Angular dimension example

Dimension line location: *pick*
Dimension text = 100
Command:

3. Continue using the tool to complete the dimensioning as shown in Fig. 11.10. The tool can be used for the vertical and horizontal dimensions.

Example 3: radius dimensions (Fig. 11.11)

1. Construct outlines such as those given in Fig. 11.11.
2. *Click* on the **Radius Dimension** in the **Dimension** toolbar:

Command:_dimradius
Select arc or circle: *pick*
Dimension line location (Mtext/Text/Angle): *pick*
Dimension text = 55
Command:

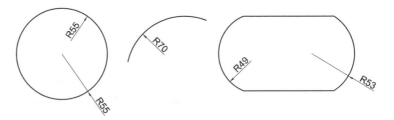

Fig. 11.11 Radial dimensions example

Example 4: baseline dimensions (Fig. 11.12)

1. Before adding baseline dimensions the set variable **DIMDLI** should be called and the required gap between the dimensions *entered* as follows:

Command: *enter* dimdli
Enter new value for DIMDLI <4>: *enter* 12
Command:

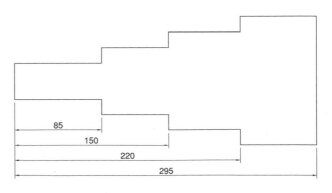

Fig. 11.12 Baseline dimension example

2. With **Linear Dimension** add the first dimension from the base-line. In this example this is the 85 dimension.
3. *Pick* the **Baseline Dimension** tool icon:

Command:_dimbaseline
Select base dimension: *pick* the 85 dimension
Select a second extension line origin: *pick*
Select a second extension line origin: *pick*
Select a second extension line origin: *pick*
Select a second extension line origin: *right-click*
Command:

Example 5: continue dimensions (Fig. 11.13)

Note: this example is taken from LT 2000; note the differences in the prompts.

1. Construct an outline such as that shown in Fig. 11.13.
2. With **Linear Dimension** place the 80 dimension.
3. *Click* on the **Continue Dimension** tool icon in the **Dimension** toolbar:

Command:_dimcontinue
Select continued dimension: *pick* the 80 linear dimension
Specify a second line origin or [Undo/Select]: *pick*
Dimension text = 115
Specify a second line origin or [Undo/Select]: *pick*
Dimension text = 140
Specify a second line origin or [Undo/Select]: *right-click*
Command:

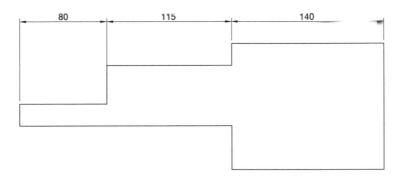

Fig. 11.13 Continue dimension example

Example 6: leader dimensions (Fig. 11.14)

1. Construct an outline such as that shown in Fig. 11.4.
2. In the **Dimension** toolbar *click* on the **Leader** tool icon:

Command:_leader
From point: *pick*
To point: *pick* **(Format/Annotation/Undo)<Annotation>:** *enter*
    CHAMFER 20 × 20 *right-click*
Command:

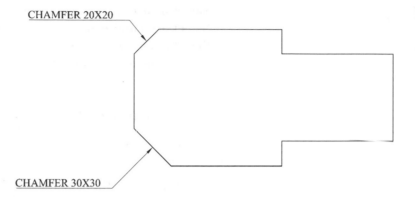

Fig. 11.14 Leader dimension
example

Dimensioning from the command line

No matter which release of AutoCAD or AutoCAD LT is in use, the following methods of adding dimensions to drawings from the command line can be used.

Note

There are two methods by which dimensions can be added to drawings from the command line, the first is to *enter* **dim** which enables dimensions of any type to be placed one after the other. *Entering* **dim1** allows dimensions to be added one at a time. In the examples which follow the **dim** command has been used. The reader is however advised to experiment with **dim1**.

Dim abbreviations

The following abbreviations are commonly used when *entering* a dimension from the command line:

hor   horizontal
ve   vertical
l   leader
al   aligned
ra   radius
d   diameter
an   angular
cen   center mark
te   tedit (same as **Dimension Text Edit** in **Dimension** toolbar)

Example 1: horizontal and vertical (Fig. 11.15)

Construct a pline outline such as that shown in Fig. 11.15. At the command line:

Command: *enter* dim *right-click*
Dim: hor
First extension line origin or RETURN to select: *pick*
Second extension line origin: *pick*
Dimension line location (Text/Angle): *pick*
Dimension text <150>: *right-click*
Dim:

      or

Command: *enter* dim *right-click*
Dim: hor
First extension line origin or RETURN to select: *right-click*
Select line, arc or circle: *pick* the line to be dimensioned
Dimension line location (Text/Angle): *pick*
Dimension text <150>: *right-click*
Dim:

    Notes

1. At the prompt **Dimension line location (Text/Angle):** if the response is **t** (Text) a dimension figure other than the **Dimension text** figure can be *entered*. In any case a different figure can be *entered* at the **Dimension text <150>:** prompt.
2. If the response is **a** (Angle) the angle of the text can be amended as shown in the **60** dimension of Fig. 11.15.
3. *Entering* **e** when in the **Dim** command ends the sequence of dimensioning.

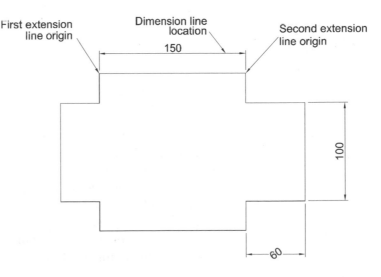

Fig. 11.15 Horizontal and vertical dimension example

Example 2: radius and diameter (Fig. 11.16)

Construct an outline such as that in Fig. 11.16. At the command line:

Command: *enter* dim *right-click*
Dim: ra (for radius)
Select arc or circle: *pick*
Dimension text <40>: *right-click*
Enter leader length: *pick*
Dim: d (for diameter)
Select arc or circle: *pick*
Dimension text <40>: *right-click*
Enter leader length: *pick*
Dim:

Note

1. At the prompt **Dimension text <40>:** a different dimension can be *entered*, but remember to add **R** for a radius or **%%C** for a diameter before the figures of the different dimension.
2. It is useful to experiment at this stage with other abbreviations in conjunction with the **dim** command at the command line.
3. Now try using the command **dim1**.

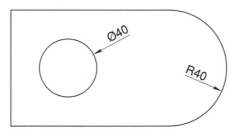

Fig. 11.16 Arc and circle dimension example

Example 3: linear tolerances (Fig. 11.19)

Before being able to include linear tolerances, new settings will need to be made in the **Dimension Styles** dialog (Releases 12–14 and AutoCAD LT 97 and LT 98) or the **Dimension Style Manager** (AutoCAD 2000 or AutoCAD LT 2000). Figure 11.17 shows the settings in the Release 14 dialog box, and Fig. 11.18 shows those in the AutoCAD 2000 or AutoCAD LT 2000 dialog boxes.

Figure 11.19 shows the dimensions with tolerances applied to a simple outline using the **hor**, **ve** and **al** responses after *entering* **dim** at the command line.

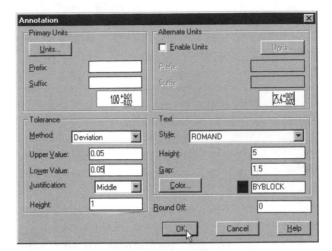

Fig. 11.17 Setting up linear
tolerances (Release 14)

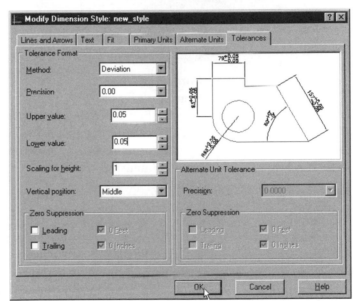

Fig. 11.18 Setting up linear
tolerances (AutoCAD 2000)

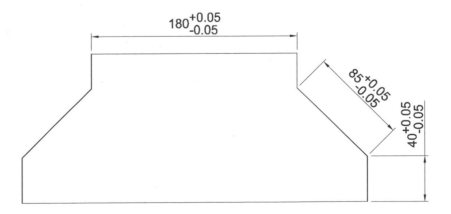

Fig. 11.19 Linear tolerances
example

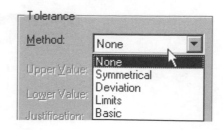

Fig. 11.20 Different methods
of linear tolerances

Figure 11.20 shows the variety of methods of linear tolerances available. *Clicking* on the **Method:** box brings up a popup list showing the possibilities. Try experimenting with the different methods available.

AutoCAD 2000 and AutoCAD LT 2000 Dim prompts

If working in either of the 2000 packages, the prompt sequences are slightly different to those shown above. As an example, when using the **Dim** command with **hor**:

Command: dim
Dim: hor
Specify first extension line origin or <select object>: *pick*
Specify second extension line origin: *pick*
Specify dimension line location or [Mtext/Text/Angle]: *right-click*
Enter dimension text <175>: *right-click*
Dim:

Questions

1. Have you tried using **tedit** (abbreviation **te**) or **Dimension Text Edit** from the **Dimension** toolbar?
2. In this chapter all dimensions have been added to drawings using text style **Romand**. Have you tried using other text styles?
3. Which do you prefer – adding dimensions using the toolbar tools, or adding dimensions using the **dim** command?
4. Are there any differences between dimensioning in AutoCAD and in AutoCAD LT?
5. When adding a diameter dimension to a drawing what should be *entered* before figures of the diameter, if the dimension to be added is different to the dimension shown?

Exercises

If you have saved drawings from worked examples of exercises in previous chapters, load them and add dimensions.

CHAPTER 12

Orthographic projection

Introduction

Despite being able to construct 3D drawings in CAD software programs (see Chapter 16 onwards), orthographic projection is still
probably the most widely used method of technical drawing. Orthographic projection relies upon viewing an object from the front, from
above, from the left or right, or from any other position relative to
the object. The object is imagined as being projected via parallel
rays onto imaginary planes perpendicular to the viewing direction;
what is drawn is the image on one of these planes.

Figure 12.1 shows the underlying principle of orthographic projection. This type of orthographic projection results in what is
known as 'first angle' projection. Figure 12.2 shows the three planes
revolved to lay on a single plane. Figure 12.3 shows the resulting
first angle projection when the planes have been removed. Remember the planes are imaginary.

The terms 'vertical plane' and 'horizontal plane' are frequently
used in connection with orthographic projection. Vertical planes

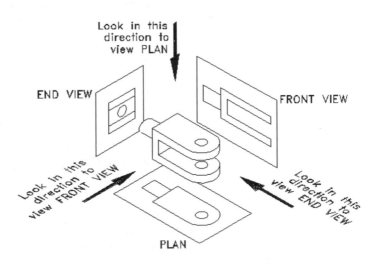

Fig. 12.1 The principles of
first angle orthographic
projection

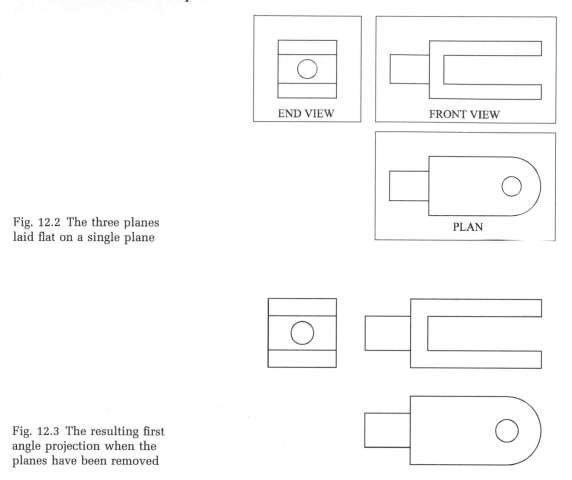

Fig. 12.2 The three planes laid flat on a single plane

Fig. 12.3 The resulting first angle projection when the planes have been removed

are those onto which front and end views have been projected. Horizontal planes are those onto which plans have been projected.

Note

1. In **first angle projection**, views and plan are placed on the opposite side to the direction in which the object is viewed. This results in the end views facing away from the front view and the plan facing away from the front view.
2. Although only three views have been shown in Figs 12.1–12.3, any number of views may be drawn in order to fully describe the object being drawn. If an object is to be constructed from a single sheet of material, only one view is needed. The more complicated the object, the more views may be necessary to fully describe its shape.

Third angle projection

Another form of orthographic projection is known as 'third angle'. Figure 12.4 shows the same object in third angle orthographic projection. In third angle the plan is above the front view and the end view is on the side from which the object has been viewed.

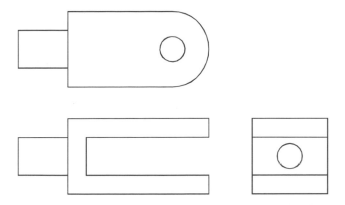

Fig. 12.4 A third angle projection

Note

In general first and third angle orthographic projections are both equally used in technical drawings. In the USA third angle is the accepted norm, but in many other countries, equal emphasis is placed on both projection.

Layers

Practically all technical drawings constructed with the aid of AutoCAD or AutoCAD LT use the concept of layers. In CAD work, layers are similar to tracings when drawing technical drawings by hand. In the same way as a tracing can be placed on the main outlines of a drawing to shows features such as centre lines, hidden detail lines, text, etc. (possibly using different colours for each tracing), so layers in CAD work can be used for similar purposes.

In architectural and building drawings a large number of layers may be used – as for example a multi-storey building may have each storey on a different layer. Electrical, plumbing and waste services may each be on a different layer, perhaps even a different set of services layers for each storey.

In this book practically all drawings have been constructed on six layers. In fact my **yarwood.dwt** template is set up with six layers. It is suggested that to continue working through the examples and exercises in later chapters that you set up similar layers in your own drawing template, following details to be given in the following pages.

Figure 12.5 shows a pictorial view of a five-layer drawing in which outlines are on layer **0**, centre lines are on layer **Centre**, hidden detail lines are on layer **Hidden**, dimensions are on layer **Dimensions** and text is on layer **Text**. The colours in which details on each layer will be drawn and the linetype associated with each layer are included in the illustration.

Figure 12.6 shows the first angle projection of the object portrayed in Fig. 12.1 as it was constructed on five layers and

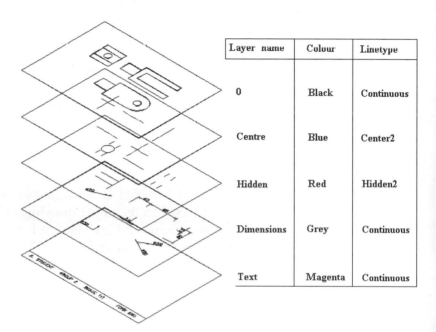

Layer name	Colour	Linetype
0	Black	Continuous
Centre	Blue	Center2
Hidden	Red	Hidden2
Dimensions	Grey	Continuous
Text	Magenta	Continuous

Fig. 12.5 A pictorial view of a five-layer drawing

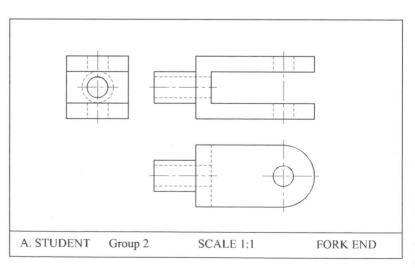

| A. STUDENT | Group 2 | SCALE 1:1 | FORK END |

Fig. 12.6 A first angle projection constructed on five layers

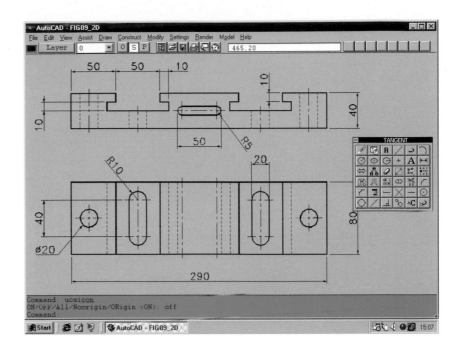

Plate I A two-view
orthographic projection in
Release 12

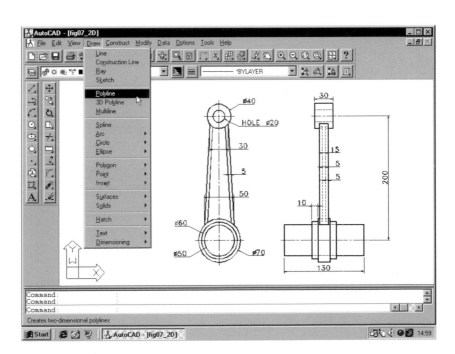

Plate II A two-view
orthographic projection in
Release 13 with the **Draw**
menu on screen

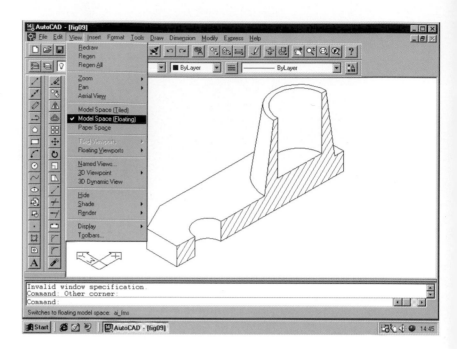

Plate III An isometric
drawing in Release 14

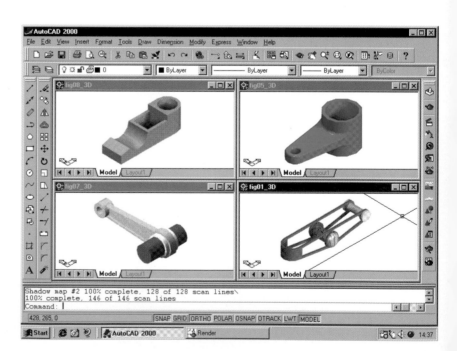

Plate IV Four renderings in
the multiple document
environment of AutoCAD
2000

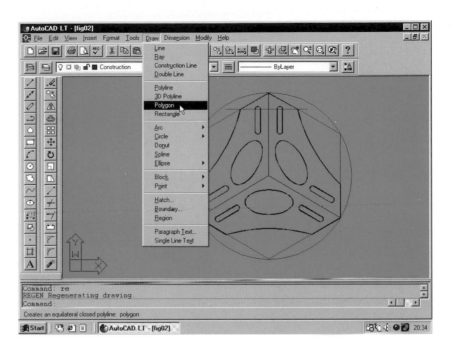

Plate V A 2D drawing in
AutoCAD LT 98 with the
Draw menu on screen

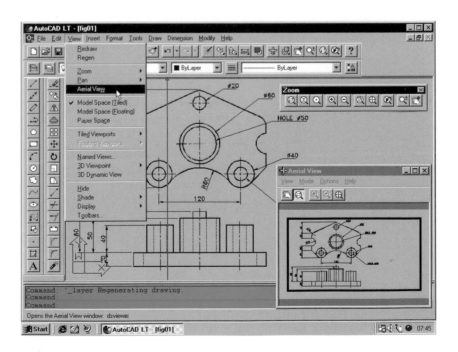

Plate VI A two-view
orthographic projection in
AutoCAD LT 2000 with the
Aerial View window on
screen and the **View** menu
displayed

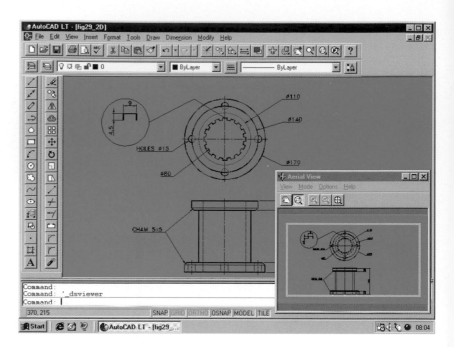

Plate VII A two-view drawing in AutoCAD LT 98 with the **Aerial View** window on screen

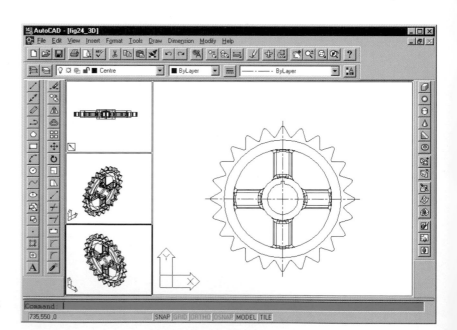

Plate VIII A four-viewport screen with a 3D model drawing being constructed in Release 14

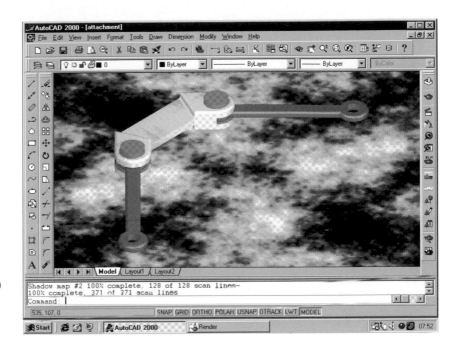

Plate IX A rendering of a 3D solid model drawing with a background in AutoCAD 2000

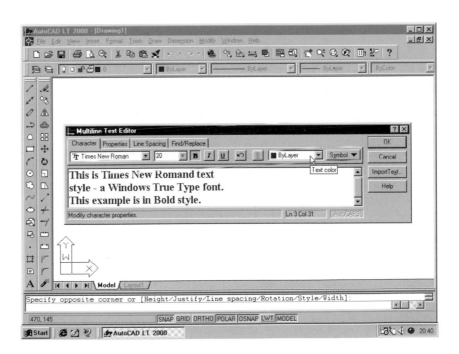

Plate X The **Multiline Text Editor** showing in AutoCAD LT 2000

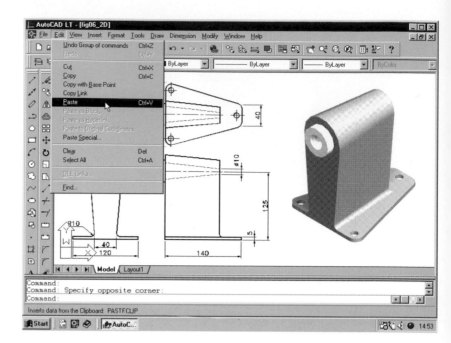

Plate XI A three-view
orthographic projection and
a bitmap in AutoCAD LT
2000

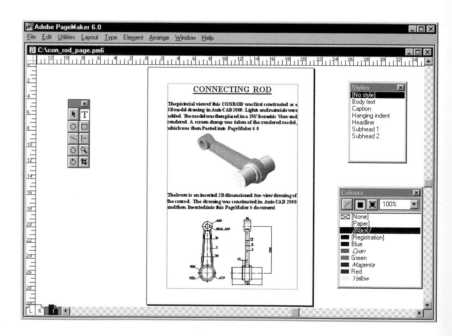

Plate XII An AutoCAD
rendering together with text
in a PageMaker document

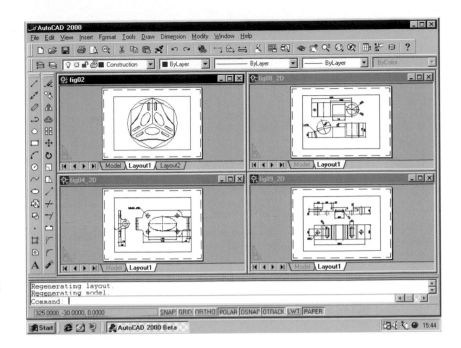

Plate XIII Four 2D drawings in the multiple document environment of AutoCAD 2000

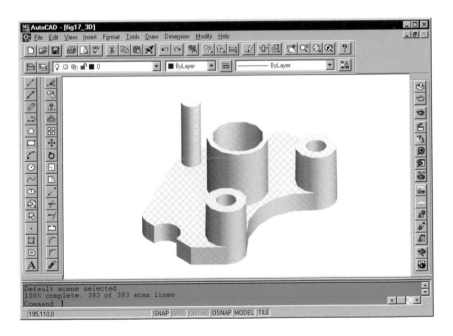

Plate XIV A rendering of a 3D model in Release 14

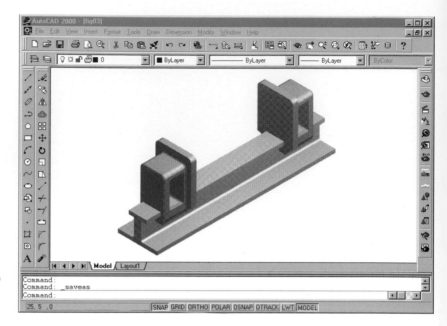

Plate XV A rendering of a 3D solid model drawing in AutoCAD 2000

Plate XVI The AutoCAD homepage

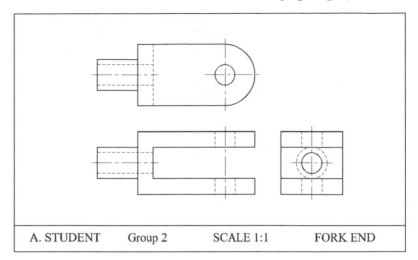

Fig. 12.7 A third angle projection constructed on five layers

| A. STUDENT | Group 2 | SCALE 1:1 | FORK END |

Fig. 12.7 shows the third angle projection of the same object. Centre lines and hidden details lines are included in these two projections.

Setting a layer

Although the methods of setting up layers in each release of AutoCAD and AutoCAD LT are different, the same basic methods are used within similar dialog boxes. Two of these dialog boxes, that for Release 14 (Fig. 12.8) and for AutoCAD 2000 (Fig. 12.9) are shown. The layer dialog boxes for AutoCAD LT are similar. Note the introduction of a **Plot** or **No Plot** icon in AutoCAD 2000 allowing details on selected layers to be plotted.

Taking the Release 14 **Layer and Linetype Properties** dialog box as an example, layers are set up in the following manner:

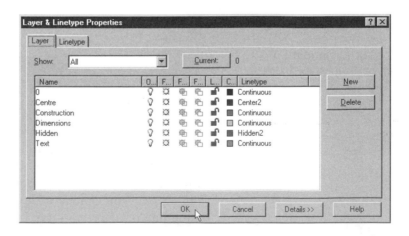

Fig. 12.8 **Layer and Linetype Properties** dialog box (Release 14)

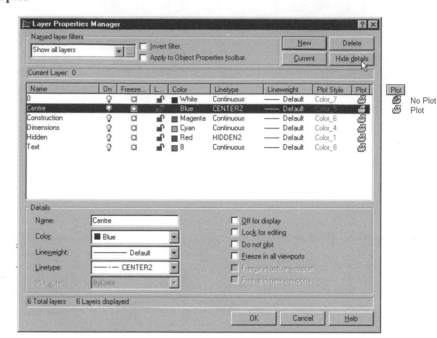

Fig. 12.9 **Layer Poperties** dialog box (AutoCAD 2000)

Fig. 12.10 **Layers** icon from the **Object Properties** toolbar

1. *Click* on the **Layers** icon in the **Object Properties** toolbar (Fig. 12.10). The **Layer and Linetype Properties** dialog box appears (Fig. 12.11). The layer **0** will already be set up – it is the default layer always present whenever AutoCAD is loaded.

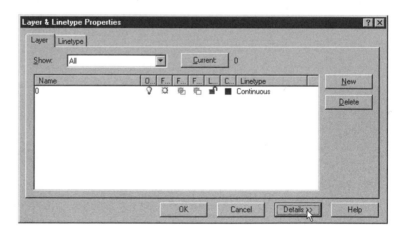

Fig. 12.11 **Layer and Linetype Properties** dialog box (Release 14)

2. If the **Details** part of the dialog is showing *click* on the **Details>>** button to turn it off.
3. *Click* on the **New** button, a default layer name **Layer1** will appear. *Click* on the **Details>>** button and in the **Details** extension of the dialog box *enter* the name **Centre** over the name **Layer1** (Fig. 12.12). The change of layer name is mirrored in the main dialog box.

Fig. 12.12 The new name
entered in the **Details Name:**
box

4. *Click* on the colour square against the name **Centre** and the **Select Color** dialog box appears (Fig. 12.13). *Double-click* on the **Blue** square in the **Standard Colors** parts of the dialog box and the colour square changes in the line of the **Centre** layer details.

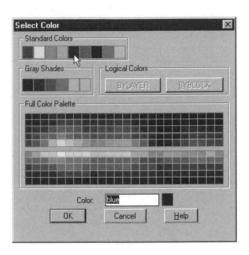

Fig. 12.13 **Select Color**
dialog box

5. *Click* on the linetype name **Continuous** against the **Centre** layer details, which brings up the **Load or Reload Linetypes** dialog box (Fig. 12.14). *Click* on the name **Center2**, followed by another on the **OK** button and yet another on the name **Center2** in the **Select Linetype** box: the linetype **Center2** appears in the **Centre** layer details.

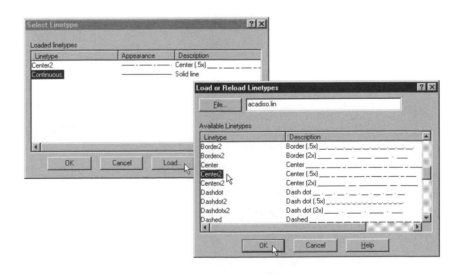

Fig. 12.14 **Select Linetype**
dialog box

6. Now set up layers **Hidden**, **Dimensions**, **Text** and **Construction** as indicated in Fig. 12.8.
7. Save the revised set of layers in your template file.

Note

1. Even though the layer dialog boxes vary between releases the steps above (or similar) will set up a set of layers in all releases.
2. Except for Release 12, in which filenames longer than 8 characters are not possible, you can can use long filenames up to 31 characters. In the 2000 series names up to 255 characters are possible. Such extended names also applies to layer names.

The Layer Control box

The **Layer Control** box in the **Objects Properties** toolbar, set below the **Standard** toolbar (usually docked at the top of the AutoCAD window), holds a number of icons which control whether a layer is **on** or **off**, **frozen** or **thawed**. You can also set the layer on which current constructions will be carried out by *clicking* on the layer name within the popup list of the **Layer Control** box.

The icons are not in the Release 12 **Layer Control** box and vary slightly between the other releases, but the effects of *clicking* on the icons shown in Fig. 12.15 are common to the other releases. The icons control layers as follows:

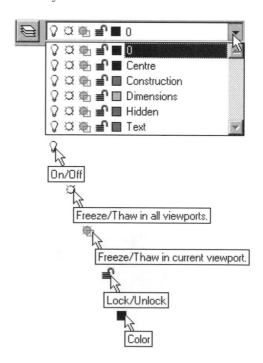

Fig. 12.15 The popup list and icons from a **Layer Control** box

On/Off: a *click* on the icon sets a layer off, another *click* will set it back on. When off the constructions on that layer do not appear on screen.

Lock/Unlock: a *click* on the icon closes the lock; another *click* opens it. Constructions can be added to a locked layer, but existing objects cannot be modified.

Freeze/Thaw: a frozen layer disappears from the drawing, but is different from a layer that has been turned off, in that screen redrawing with frozen layers is faster than if the layers had simply been turned off. This is of particular use when a layer contains a great deal of construction.

Color: shows the colours in which objects will appear when added to the layer.

Note

Layers can be set up from the command line, but it is usually much quicker to use the various layer dialog boxes for this purpose.

Example of an orthographic projection

Figure 12.16 shows a rendering of a 3D model of a rod support. A third angle orthographic projection of the rod support is to be constructed.

Fig. 12.16 Rendering of a 3D model of a rod support

1. Open a drawing template with layers set up as described above. Layer **0** will, by default, be the current layer.

2. Within the popup list of the **Layer Control** box, *click* on **Construction** to make that layer current (Fig. 12.17).

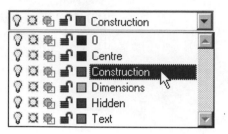

Fig. 12.17 Setting the layer **Construction** as the current layer

Fig. 12.18 The **Construction Line** tool icon

3. *Click* on the **Construction Line** tool icon in the **Draw** toolbar (Fig. 12.18). Construction lines are lines of infinite length, which can be drawn vertically, horizontally or at any angle.
4. Draw construction lines as indicated in Fig. 12.19. The positions of the construction lines will need to be worked out in advance.
5. Make layer **0** the current layer.

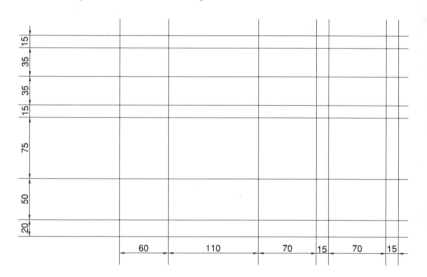

Fig. 12.19 The construction lines on which the three views are to be based

6. With the **Polyline** tool construct the outlines over the construction lines as shown in Fig. 12.20. In this example the pline width has been set to 0.7.
7. Turn the **Construction** layer off. Make the **Centre** layer current.
8. Add all centre lines through each of the circular parts (Fig. 12.21).
9. Make the **Hidden** layer current and add all hidden detail lines (Fig. 12.22).
10. Make the **Dimensions** layer current and add all dimensions (Fig. 12.23).
11. Make the **Text** layer current and add a border and a title block (Fig. 12.24).

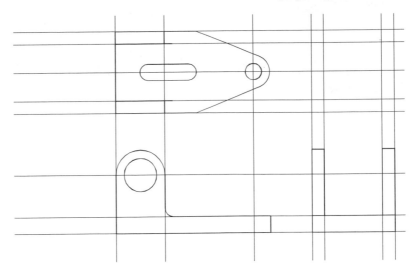

Fig. 12.20 The view
outlines drawn over the
construction lines

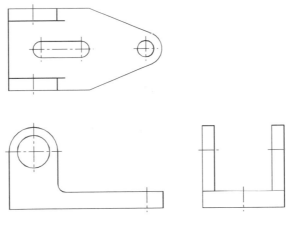

Fig. 12.21 Add centre lines

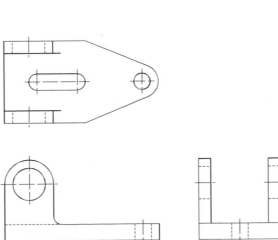

Fig. 12.22 Add hidden
detail lines

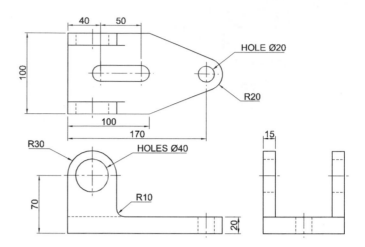

Fig. 12.23 Add dimensions

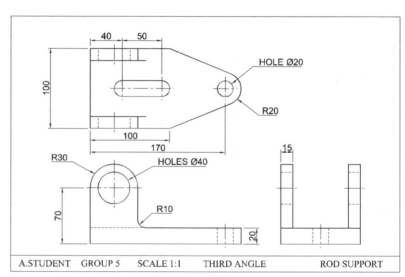

| A.STUDENT   GROUP 5   SCALE 1:1   THIRD ANGLE   ROD SUPPORT |

Fig. 12.24 The completed
orthographic projection

Notes

1. Centre lines are drawn through circular parts in all three directions in which the part is viewed.
2. Hidden detail lines show parts which cannot be seen in outside views.
3. The border and title block shown in Fig. 12.24 are simple additions suitable for students working in colleges or pupils working in schools.

Questions

1. The word 'orthogonal' means 'perpendicular' or 'at right angles'. Can you explain why orthographic projection is so named?

2. There are two main methods of orthographic projection: first angle and third angle. Can you explain the differences between two three-view orthographic projections, one in first angle, the other in third angle?
3. What is the **Construction Line** tool used for?
4. What are layers?
5. What is the purpose of layers?
6. What is the quickest method of turning a layer off when working in AutoCAD or AutoCAD LT?
7. What is the difference between a layer turned off and a frozen layer?
8. Have you added the layers described in this chapter to your template file?
9. What is the purpose of centre lines?
10. What is the purpose of hidden detail lines?

Exercises

1. Figure 12.25 shows a rendering of a 3D model. Figure 12.26 is a two-view third angle orthographic projection of the part. Construct

Fig. 12.25 Exercise 1 – a rendering

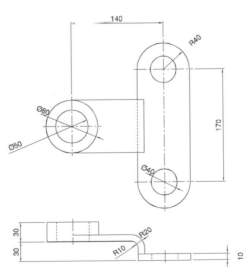

Fig. 12.26 Exercise 1

a three-view first angle projection of the part, complete with all dimensions, and add a suitable border and title block.

2. Figure 12.27 shows a rendering of a 3D model. Figure 12.28 is a two-view first angle projection of the part. Construct a fully dimensioned three-view third angle orthographic projection of the part, working to full size. Add a suitable border and title block.

Fig. 12.27 Exercise 2 – a rendering

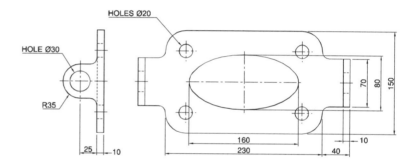

Fig. 12.28 Exercise 2

3. Figure 12.29 shows a rendering of a 3D model. Figure 12.30 is a two-view orthographic projection of the part. Construct a fully dimensioned three-view orthographic projection of the part.

Fig. 12.29 Exercise 3 – a rendering

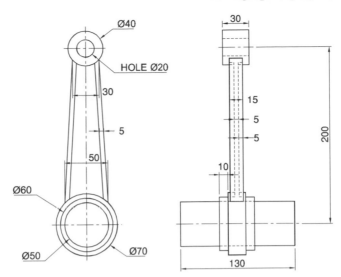

Fig. 12.30 Exercise 3

4. Figure 12.31 shows a rendering of a 3D model. Figure 12.32 is a two-view third angle orthographic projection of the part. Construct a fully dimensioned three-view first angle projection of the part. Add a suitable border and title block.

Fig. 12.31 Exercise 4 – a
rendering

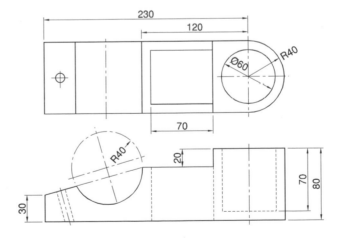

Fig. 12.32 Exercise 4

5. Figure 12.33 shows a rendering and a two-view orthographic projection of a handle. Working to the sizes given construct a full-size, fully dimensioned three-view third angle orthographic projection of the handle.

Fig. 12.33 Exercise 5 – a rendering and a two-view projection

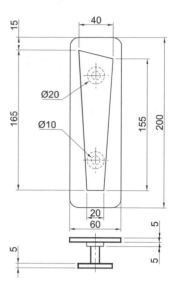

CHAPTER 13

Isometric drawing

Introduction

Isometric drawing is a form of pictorial drawing that must not be confused with 3D drawings (see Chapter 16 onwards). Isometric drawings, despite their 3D appearance are flat 2D constructions. The basic features of this form of drawing are shown in Fig. 13.1, in which a rectangular prism with a central hole is shown together with the angles at which non-vertical lines are drawn.

Setting up AutoCAD for isometric drawing

To set up the drawing area of any of the AutoCAD windows, set **Snap** as follows:

Command: *enter* snap *right-click*
Snap spacing or (ON/OFF/Aspect/Rotate/Style: <10>: *enter* s *right-click*
Standard/Isometric <S>: *enter* i *right-click*
Command:

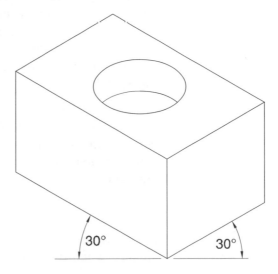

Fig. 13.1 The angles on which isometric drawings are based

The AutoCAD window changes as shown in Fig. 13.2. Although this illustration was taken from a Release 14 window, the other releases look the same when **Snap** is set to **Isometric**.

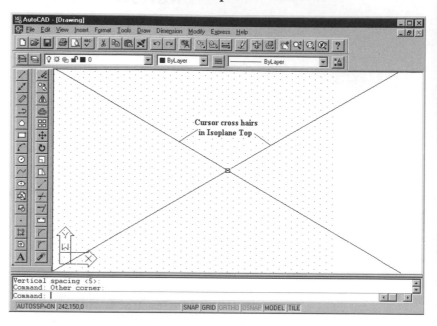

Fig. 13.2 AutoCAD window in **Isometric** snap mode

The isometric isoplanes

While in isometric mode hold down the **Ctrl** key and press the **E** key. The command line shows **<Isoplane Left>**, **<Isoplane Top>** and **<Isoplane Right>** with each successive press of **Ctrl+E**. The cursor hairs respond to this as shown in Figs 13.2 and 13.3. The same result is obtained by repeatedly pressing function key **F5**.

Figure 13.4 shows a cube constructed in the three isoplanes with an isometric ellipse centred on each face. In order to ensure an ellipse is correctly positioned in an isoplane face change the current isoplane as required using **Ctrl+E** or **F5**. Then call the **Ellipse** tool:

Command:_ellipse
<Axis endpoint 1>/Center/Isocircle: *enter* i *right-click*
Center of circle: *pick*
<Circle radius>/Diameter: *pick*
Command:

Note

The **Isocircle** prompt only appears during the **Ellipse** prompt sequence when the screen is in an **Isoplane**.

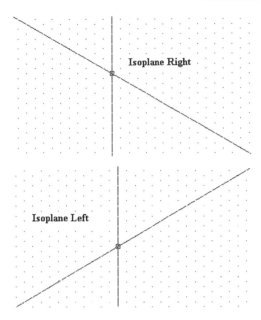

Fig. 13.3 The cursor hairs in **Isoplane Right** and **Isoplane Left**

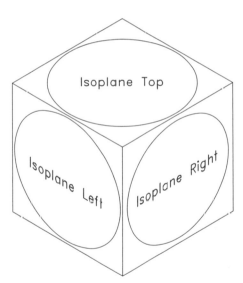

Fig. 13.4 The three Isoplanes

Example of an isometric drawing

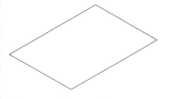

Fig. 13.5 Example – stage 3

1. Set **Snap** to an isometric style.
2. Press **F5** until **Isoplane Top** is selected.
3. Call the **Polyline** tool and construct an isometric rectangle 140 × 100 as in Fig. 13.5.
4. Press **F5** to select **Isoplane Right**.
5. With **Polyline** add the outlines as in Fig. 13.6.
6. Press **F5** to select **Isoplane Left**.

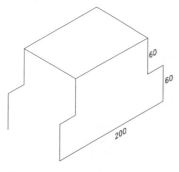

Fig. 13.6 Example – stage 5

7. Add plines as in Fig. 13.7.
8. Add isometric circles of radius 20 as shown in Fig. 13.8.
9. Add recesses as shown in Fig. 13.8, each recess set in 20 from edges and 10 deep.
10. It will be necessary to use **Trim** to trim away parts of the isometric circles at the bottoms of the two circular recesses.

A number of exercises follow for the reader to practise using isometric drawing methods. At first sight some of these may appear difficult, but isometric drawing in AutoCAD is comparatively easy.

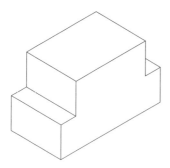

Fig. 13.7 Example – stage 7

Fig. 13.8 The completed isometric drawing

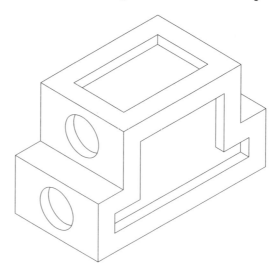

Exercises

1. Figure 13.9 shows the isometric drawing resulting from following the details in Fig. 13.10. Construct the isometric drawing to the details given in Fig. 13.10.

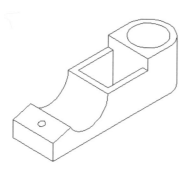

Fig. 13.9 Exercise 1 – isometric drawing

Fig. 13.10 Exercise 1

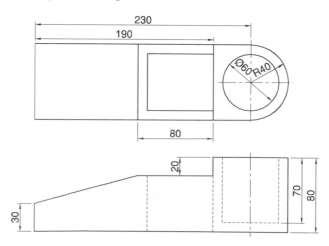

2. Construct an isometric drawing of the part shown in the two-
view first angle projection of Fig. 13.11.

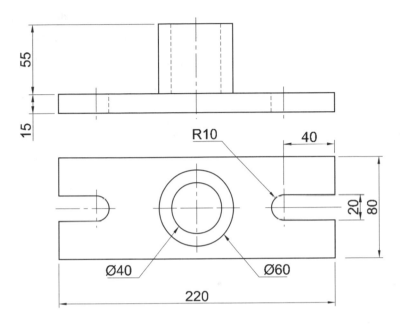

Fig. 13.11 Exercise 2

3. Construct an isometric drawing of the part shown in the two-
view orthographic projection of Fig. 13.12.

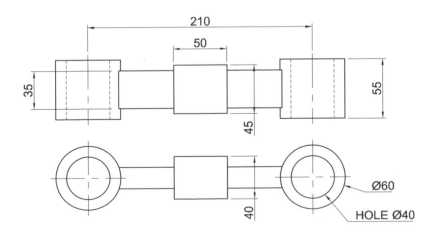

Fig. 13.12 Exercise 3

4. Figure 13.13 is a three-view orthographic drawing. Construct an isometric drawing to the dimensions given in the projection.

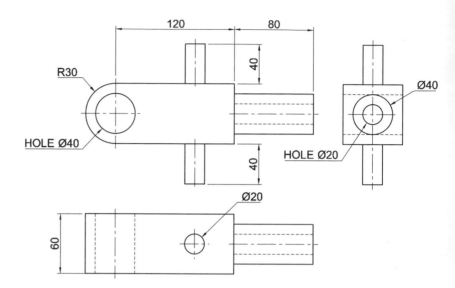

Fig. 13.13 Exercise 4

CHAPTER 14

Blocks and Inserts

Introduction

Part or all of any AutoCAD drawing (with the filename extension ***.dwg**) can be inserted into any other drawing or can be saved as a 'block' for insertion into another drawing. Although the dialog boxes vary somewhat between the various releases of AutoCAD and AutoCAD LT, the methods used for making and inserting blocks are very similar.

Blocks

There are two types of block which can be inserted into drawings. The **Make Block** tool creates a block that becomes part of the data of the drawing in which it is saved. The other type of block – a 'written block' or 'wblock' – is saved as an independent drawing and only becomes part of the data of a drawing after it has been inserted into a drawing. It is important to understand the difference between these two types of blocks. Quite apart from blocks and wblocks, any drawing or part of a drawing which has been saved in a separate drawing file with its own filename can be inserted into another drawing.

The Block and Make Block tools

Up to and including Release 14 and AutoCAD LT 98, blocks could be made by *entering* **block** at the command line and *entering* responses as appropriate. From Release 14 onwards, the tool **Make Block** (abbreviation **b**) was introduced. *Clicking* the tool icon brings up a dialog box in which parameters for making a block can be set. When making a block using the command line method the procedures are the same as when using the dialog box.

If the **Block** tool icon of Release 12 or 13 is selected, no dialog box appears and all responses must be made at the command line.

Block tool icon Release 12

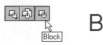

Block tool icon Release 13

Block tool icon Release 14 and 2000

Fig. 14.1 Calling the **Block** and **Make Block** tools

Fig. 14.2 Using the **Make Block** tool (Release 14)

Example: making a block

The following is a description of making a block using the Release 14 **Block Definition** dialog box. Note however that in AutoCAD 2000 and AutoCAD LT 2000 the dialog box is different, although the methods of forming a block are similar.

1. Construct the drawing which is to become a block. In the example given in Fig. 14.2 four electronics symbols have been constructed. The upper of the four symbols is that for a battery.

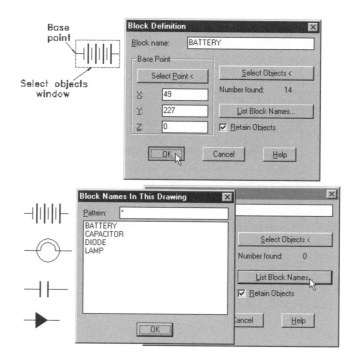

2. *Click* on the **Make Block** tool. The **Block Definition** dialog box appears (upper part of Fig. 14.2).
3. In the dialog box *enter* the block name (**BATTERY**) in the **Block Name:** box, followed by a *click* on the **Select Objects<** button. The dialog box disappears, allowing the operator to 'window' the battery drawing. *Right-click* and the dialog box reappears.
4. *Click* on the **Select Point<** button and select a point on the battery symbol. This point is the insertion point used when the block is inserted, in this case into a circuit diagram. It should therefore be chosen with care, preferably using the **endpoint** osnap, which will allow the block to be accurately positioned in the circuit.
5. Finally *click* on the **OK** button of the dialog box.

Notes

1. If this procedure is carried out with a number of symbols (or any other form of drawing), when the **Insert** tool is called and its dialog box appears, a *click* on the **Block** button will bring up the **Block Names in This Drawing** dialog, which lists the blocks held in the current drawing. This is shown in the bottom part of Fig. 14.2.
2. Because the creation of blocks plays such an important part in CAD drawing each release of AutoCAD has revised and updated the **Block** tool. However the methods of creating a block have not changed significantly. Parameters for making a block are the same whether working from the command line or using the dialog boxes from different releases.

Example: making a wblock

Note: there is no **wblock** tool icon. In this example the same symbols are used as in the previous example. First, construct suitable symbols or other drawings. Then, at the Command line:

Command: *enter* w (or wblock) *right-click*

The **Create Drawing File** dialog box appears (Fig. 14.3). *Enter* a suitable filename in the **File Name:** box. Select a suitable directory into which the file should be saved *click* on **OK** (or **Save** in some releases).
    The command line then shows:

Block name: *right-click*
Insertion base point: *pick*
Select objects: *pick* (in a window if necessary)
Command:

The symbol (or other form of drawing) is saved independently of the drawing on screen.

Fig. 14.3 Creating a **wblock** (the **Create Drawing File** dialog box)

Note

The abbreviation **w** for **wblock** will have to be added to the **acad.pgp** file for Release 12 and 13.

The Insert tool

Inserting a drawing or a block into a drawing involves the use of the **Insert** or **Insert Block** tool. Settings for inserting blocks are made in the **Insert** dialog box. This box varies somewhat between releases, but the settings in the box are similar throughout the releases. No matter which release is in use *entering* **ddinsert** at the command line will bring up the dialog box.

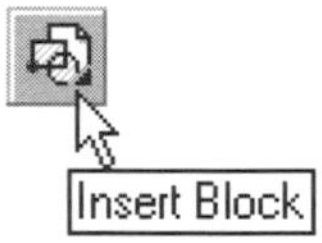

There is no **Insert Block** tool icon in Release 12, but in later releases of both AutoCAD and AutoCAD LT a *click* on the **Insert Block** tool icon in the **Draw** toolbar (Fig. 14.4) brings up the **Insert** dialog box (Fig. 14.5). This illustration shows the dialog box from Release 14; although in other releases the box is slightly different, individual settings in the box are similar.

Fig. 14.4 **Insert Block** tool icon

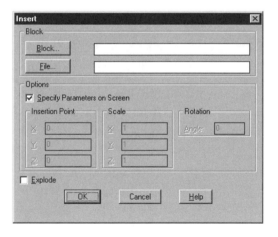

Fig. 14.5 **Insert** dialog box

Example: inserting wblocks

1. Construct a group of electronics symbols as shown in Fig. 14.6.
2. Save each symbol separately as a wblock to a suitable directory. In this example, this directory is **C:\electrics**.
3. Call the **Insert Block** tool. The **Insert** dialog box appears. *Click* on the **File ...** button which brings up the **Select Drawing File** dialog box. Select the directory **C:\electrics** and the saved wblocks appear in the file list. *Double-click* on **battery.dwg** (Fig. 14.7). The name appears in the **Block ...** and **File ...** boxes (Fig. 14.8).

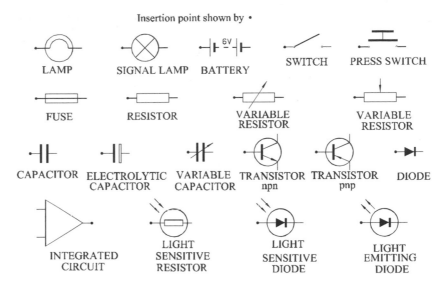

Insertion point shown by •
LAMP
SIGNAL LAMP
6V
BATTERY
SWITCH
PRESS SWITCH
FUSE
RESISTOR
VARIABLE RESISTOR
VARIABLE RESISTOR
CAPACITOR
ELECTROLYTIC CAPACITOR
VARIABLE CAPACITOR
TRANSISTOR npn
TRANSISTOR pnp
DIODE
INTEGRATED CIRCUIT
LIGHT SENSITIVE RESISTOR
LIGHT SENSITIVE DIODE
LIGHT EMITTING DIODE

Fig. 14.6 Electronic symbols to be saved as wblocks

Block
Block...
File...
Select Drawing File
Look in: electrics
Preview
battery
capac
diode
fuse
int
lamp
lsd
lsr
npn
pnp
press_sw
resist
signal
switch
var_cap
var_res
File name: battery
Files of type: Drawing (*.dwg)
Open
Cancel
Find File...
Locate

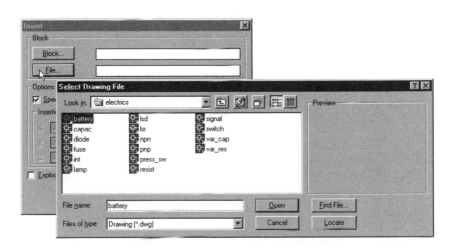

Fig. 14.7 Selecting **battery.dwg** for insertion

Insert
Block
Block...
BATTERY
File...
C:\electrics\battery.DWG
Options
Specify Parameters on Screen
Insertion Point
Scale
Rotation
X: 0
Y: 0
Z: 0
X: 1
Y: 1
Z: 1
Angle: 0
Explode
OK
Cancel
Help

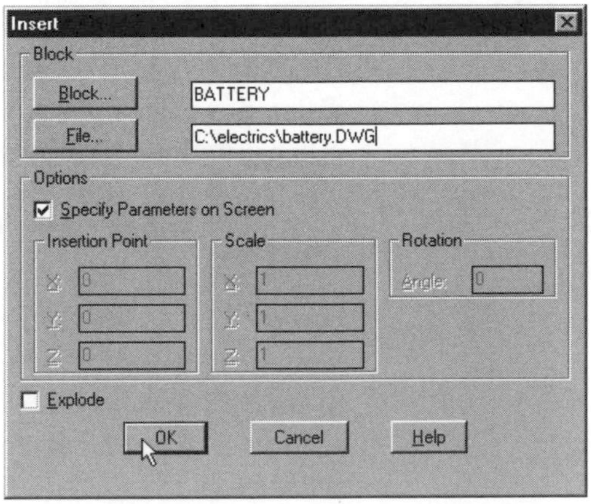

Fig. 14.8 The wblock name appearing in the **Insert** dialog box

4. *Click* on the **OK** button of the **Insert** dialog box and the battery symbol appears on screen and can be *dragged* into position via its insertion point. The command line shows:

Command:_ddinsert
Insertion point: *pick*
X scale factor <1>/Corner/XYZ: *right-click*
Y scale factor (default = X): *right-click*
Rotation angle <0>: *right-click*
Command:

5. Repeat with the **lamp**, **npn** (rotation 90), **resist** (three times with one rotated at 90) and **switch** (rotation 90), inserting each in a suitable position.

6. Add conductor lines and donuts at intersection points as necessary to complete the circuit diagram. The left-hand resistor will need to be changed into a variable resistor (Fig. 14.9).

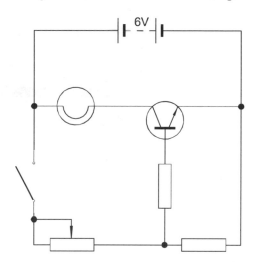

Fig. 14.9 A circuit constructed from wblock drawings

External references

External references (xrefs) are another form of block with the crucial difference that if the xref is changed after it has been inserted into another drawing, the version of the xref in the drawing changes as well.

Example: xrefs (Figs 14.10–14.18)

The method of including an xref within a drawing varies somewhat between releases. In Release 12 the whole operation must be carried out at the command line. In Release 13 a dialog box (**Select file to attach**) appears from which a drawing can be selected. In later releases the **External Reference** dialog box appears. In this example Release 14 is in use, but other releases follow the same sequence of operations.

1. Figure 14.10 is a two-view orthographic projection of a rectangular plate in which two holes have been bored. A front view and a sectional view are included.

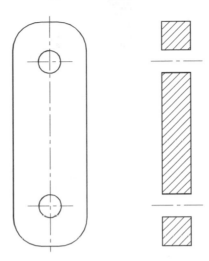

Fig. 14.10 Example – stage 1

Fig. 14.11 Two views of a bolt saved as separate wblocks

2. Figure 14.11 shows drawings of two views of a bolt and its head. These have been saved as separate drawings as wblocks.
3. With the two views of the rectangular plate on screen and ensuring the current layer is layer **0**, *enter* at the command line:

Command: *enter* xref *right-click*

The **External Reference** dialog box appears (Fig. 14.12). *Click* on the **Attach . . .** button. The **Select file to attach** dialog box appears (Fig. 14.13), from which the drawing **Bolt** is selected. The **Attach Xref** dialog box appears (Fig. 14.14), with the name of the selected drawing file name in the **Xref Name** box. *Click* on the **OK** button. The dialog box disappears and the **bolt** drawing appears and can be *dragged* by its insertion point (Fig. 14.15).

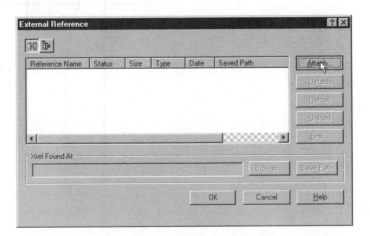

Fig. 14.12 **External Reference** dialog box

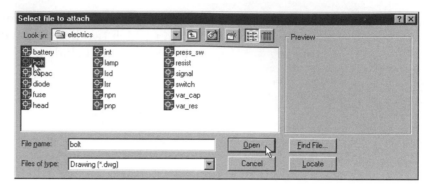

Fig. 14.13 **Select file to attach** dialog box

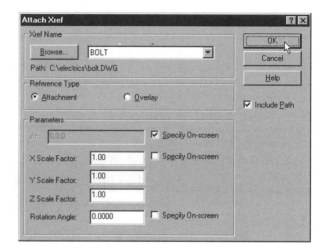

Fig. 14.14 **Attach Xref** dialog box

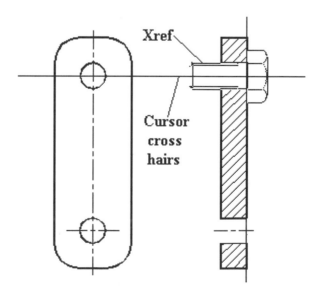

Fig. 14.15 The Xref being *dragged* into position

4. *Drag* the bolt to its required insertion point in the drawing and *left-click*.
5. Repeat with the bolt and with the **head** drawing – to give Fig. 14.17.
6. Save the drawing with its xrefs.
7. Change the **bolt** and **head** drawings as shown in Fig. 14.16 and save them to the same file names.

Fig. 14.16 Changes to the **bolt** and **head** drawings

8. Now open the original two-view drawing with its xrefs. The revisions made to the bolt and head drawings have been incorporated in the drawing (Fig. 14.18).

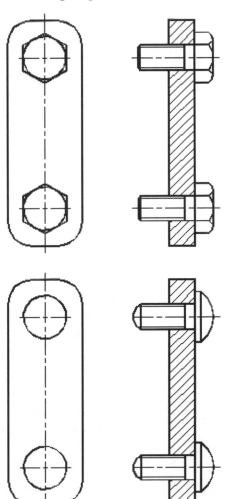

Fig. 14.17 The four xrefs in position

Fig. 14.18 The revised **bolt** and **head** xrefs in the two-view orthographic projection

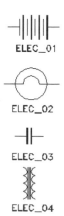

Fig. 14.19 Four electronic symbols

Example: attributes (Figs 14.19–14.23)

1. Construct the four electronics symbols shown in Fig. 14.19.
2. Save each in turn as wblocks with filenames **elec_01**, **elec_02**, **elec_03** and **elec_04**.
3. Open a new drawing and open each of the four symbol drawings in turn.
4. At the command line:

   Command: *enter* ddattdef *right-click*

   The **Attribute Definition** dialog box appears. Make entries in the dialog box as shown in Fig. 14.20.

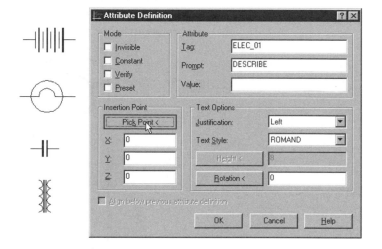

Fig. 14.20 **Attribute Definition** dialog box

5. *Click* on the **Pick Point<** button and *pick* a point under the uppermost symbol. The dialog box reappears. *Click* on the **OK** button and the name **ELEC_01** appears at the *picked* point.
6. Repeat item **5** with each of the other symbols, *entering* **ELEC_02**, **ELEC_03** and **ELEC_04** in the **Tag:** box as appropriate. The four symbols now have tags as shown in Fig. 14.21.
7. Call **Insert Block** tool:

   Command: the **Insert** dialog box appears. Select the drawing with the filename **elec_02** and *click* on the **OK** button (Fig. 14.22)
   INSERT
   Specify insertion point: *pick*
   Enter attribute values
   DESCRIBE: *enter* LAMP
   Command:

   The symbol **elec_02** appears on screen with the attribute **LAMP** in place of **ELEC_02**.

Fig. 14.21 The four symbols and their tags

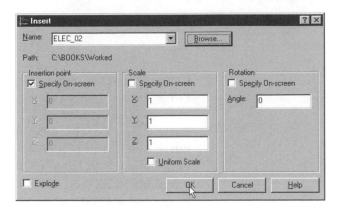

Fig. 14.22 The **Insert** dialog box

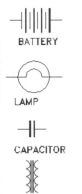

Fig. 14.23 The four symbols and their appropriate attribute tags

Fig. 14.24 **AutoCAD Text Window** showing blocks in a drawing

8. Repeat with each of the other symbols (the result is shown in Fig. 14.23).

Note

This method of adding attribute tags to drawings is common the all the Windows versions of AutoCAD and AutoCAD LT covered by this book.

The Purge tool

The **Purge** tool can be used to remove unwanted data from a drawing file. This reduces the size of the file on disk and can save considerable disk space. It is of particular importance in clearing the data created by either saving numerous blocks within a drawing or by the insertion of blocks. Take for example the drawing file of Fig. 14.6; if each individual symbol had been saved as a block the total bytes in the file would have been 25 kilobytes. After purging the file became only 8 kilobytes.

Example: Purge

To check the blocks in the drawing:

Command: *enter* blocks *right-click*
Block name (or ?): *enter* ? *right-click*
Block(s) to list<*>: *right-click*

An **AutoCAD Text Window** appears listing the blocks in the drawing (Fig. 14.24). *Click* on the **Close** button of the window and the command line reverts to:

Command:

Now purge all unwanted data from the drawing:

Command: *enter* purge *right-click*
Purge unused blocks/Dimstyles/LAyers/LTypes/SHapes/STyles/All:
    enter a (All) *right-click*
Purge block LAMP? <N>: *enter* y *right-click*
Purge block BATTERY? <N>: *enter* y *right-click*
Purge block SWITCH? <N>: *enter* y *right-click*
Purge block PRESS? <N>: *enter* y *right-click*
Purge block FUSE? <N>: *enter* y *right-click*

And so on until all blocks are purged.

Purge layer HIDDEN? <N>: *enter* y *right-click*
Purge layer CENTRE? <N>: *enter* y *right-click*
Purge linetype CENTER2? <N>: *enter* y *right-click*
Purge dimension style STANDARD? <N>: *enter* y *right-click*
Command:

The Explode tool

In the **Insert** dialog box (Fig. 14.25) you will see a check box labelled **Explode**. If the check box is set 'on' (tick in box) with a *left-click*, the block will be inserted with all its original objects ungrouped. If the **Explode** check box is left 'off' (without a tick), the block will be inserted as a single object and can be moved around the screen as a single object.

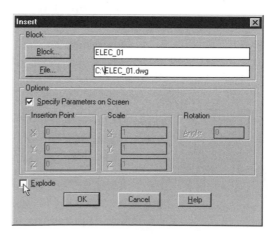

Fig. 14.25 **Insert** dialog box and the **Explode** checkbox

Release 12 **Explode**

X

Explode

Other releases

Fig. 14.26 Calling the **Explode** tool

Another way of exploding a block, or other object formed from a number of objects, is to call the **Explode** tool, either by *entering* **x** or **explode** at the command line or with a *click* on the **Explode** tool icon in the **Modify** toolbar (Fig. 14.26).

Command:_explode
Select objects: *pick*
Command:

The *picked* object is exploded into its constituent objects.

Questions

1. What is the difference between a block and a wblock?
2. What does wblock stand for?
3. What is meant by 'exploding' an object?
4. How can unwanted data in the form of blocks, etc. be removed from a file when a drawing is saved?
5. How does an external reference (an xref) differ from a block when it is inserted into a drawing?
6. What is an attribute?
7. When making a wblock, why is it important to make sure its insertion point is carefully chosen?
8. If you are using AutoCAD LT 97 or 98 the **Content Explorer** can be used for inserting blocks. In the same way, if using AutoCAD 2000 or AutoCAD LT 2000, the **AutoCAD Design Center** can be used for inserting blocks. If you are using any of these releases, have you tried using the **Content Explorer** or the **AutoCAD Design Center**?

Exercises

1. Figure 14.27 is a simple electronic circuit. If you have not already constructed Fig. 14.6 and saved each symbol as a separate wblock, do so now. Using these wblocks construct the circuit diagram in Fig. 14.27. Add the text as shown.
2. Figures 14.28–14.30 show a sectional view through a flange with a pin inserted as an xref. With subsequent amendment of the xref, the drawing is amended as shown in the right-hand drawing of Fig. 14.30. Construct the two drawings Figs 14.28 and 14.29. Save both drawings with suitable filenames. Insert Fig. 14.29 twice as an xref into Fig. 14.28. Then call up the pin drawing and amend as shown in Fig. 14.30. Call back the drawing for Fig. 14.28 to see the amended pins.

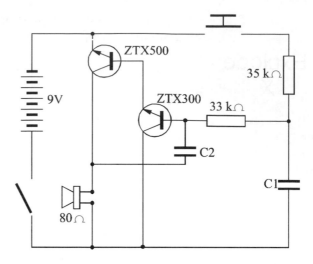

Fig. 14.27 Exercise 1

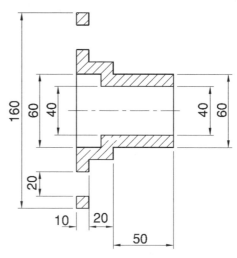

Fig. 14.28 Exercise 2 –
drawing into which the xref
is inserted

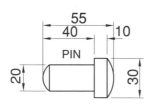

Fig. 14.29 The pin inserted
as an xref

Fig. 14.30 Exercise 2
showing the amended xref

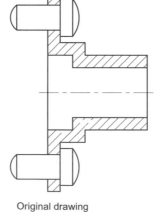

Original drawing
with XREF

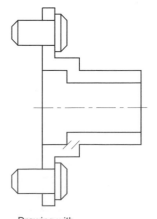

Drawing with
amended XREF

3. Figure 14.31 is a view of a bolt with the tag **BOLT_01**. Construct a drawing of a similar bolt and save it with a suitable filename. Then, using the **Attribute Definition** dialog box and the **Insert** tool, insert the bolt with the name 'NEW BOLT'.

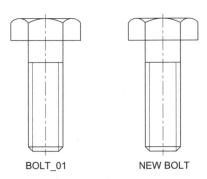

BOLT_01   NEW BOLT

Fig. 14.31 Exercise 3

4. Figure 14.32 is a view of a countersunk screw. Construct a similar drawing and give it a tag. Then, using the **Attribute Definition** dialog box and the **Insert** tool, insert the screw with a name based on the tag.
5. Construct a number of rectangles as 'cards' on which names, addresses and telephone numbers can be printed. The cards each carry the tags as shown. Using the **Attributes Definition** dialog box, make up a series of cards carrying your friends' names, addresses and telephone numbers.

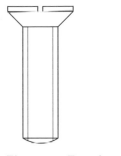

Fig. 14.32 Exercise 4

NAME
ADDRESS
TEL:

Fig. 14.33 Exercise 5

CHAPTER 15

Object linking and embedding

Introduction

Object linking and embedding (OLE) allows graphics and/or text files from one application to be pasted into documents of another application, or linked with documents from another application. For example an AutoCAD drawing can be pasted into (embedded or linked) applications such as word processing packages and desktop publishing packages. It also means that in any of the releases of AutoCAD with which we are concerned here, graphic images and text from other applications can be pasted into or linked with AutoCAD drawings. There is a distinct difference between objects that are embedded and objects that are linked.

Embedded objects

When a graphic or text object is embedded, usually (but not always) using the **Paste** command common to all Windows applications, there are no links between the original object and the embedded/pasted object. Changes subsequently made to the original are not seen in the embedded object.

Linked objects

When a graphic or text object is linked changes made to the original automatically update the linked object. Thus, if an AutoCAD drawing is linked to a document in a desktop publishing application, any subsequent changes made to the AutoCAD drawing in AutoCAD also appear in the linked object within the desktop publishing document.

The Edit menu

Figure 15.1 shows the **Edit** menu from each of the releases of AutoCAD. Note the similarity between the four menus (only part of the Release 12 and 13 menus are shown). The **Edit** menus from AutoCAD LT are similar.

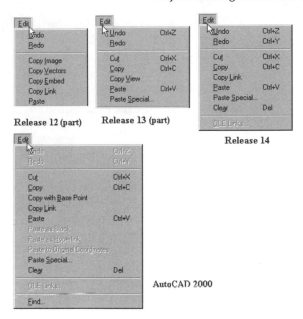

Fig. 15.1 **Edit** menus from four releases of AutoCAD

Examples of OLE

Example: pasting a bitmap into an AutoCAD drawing (Figures 15.2–15.4)

Note this facility is not available in Release 12. If an attempt is made to paste a bitmap into a Release 12 drawing, nothing will appear on the Release 12 screen.

1. Construct a 3D model drawing (Chapter 16) of the part shown in the orthographic drawing of Fig. 15.2. Add lights and materials and render the model (Chapter 20). With the aid of a screenshot application save the rendered model as a bitmap.

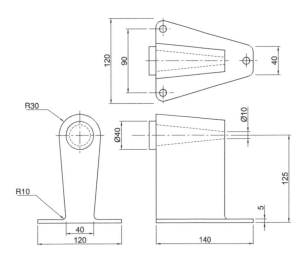

Fig. 15.2 Two-view drawing constructed in AutoCAD

2. Construct the drawing Fig. 15.2.
3. Open the bitmap in the Windows' **Paint** application. From the **Edit** menu *click* on **Select All**, then on **Copy** (see Fig. 15.3).
4. Open the two-view drawing and *click* on **Paste** in the **Edit** menu. The bitmap appears within a frame. The frame allows re-sizing and moving of the bitmap to its desired size and position.

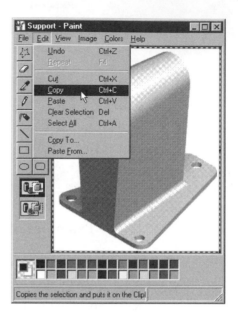

Fig. 15.3 The screenshot bitmap in **Paint**; note the broken line indicating that **Select All** has been chosen from the **Edit** menu

Figure 15.4 shows the resulting drawing and bitmap in a Release 13 window. Colour plate XI also shows this AutoCAD window.

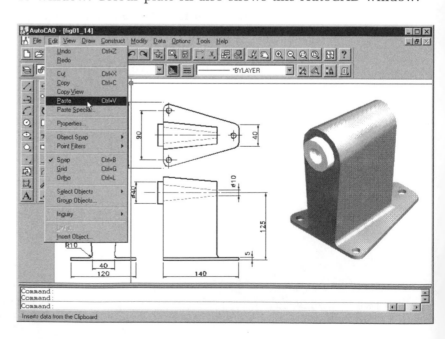

Fig. 15.4 Two-view drawing and a bitmap pasted into an AutoCAD Release 13 window

Example: linking AutoCAD drawings to a PageMaker document (Figures 15.5–15.7)

Figure 15.5 shows two AutoCAD drawings which have been inserted into a PageMaker document.

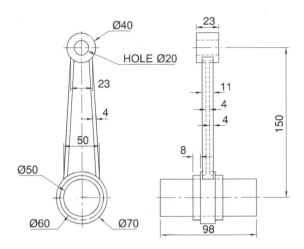

Fig. 15.5 Two-view drawing of a connecting rod (conrod)

1. Construct the two drawings Figs 15.5 and 15.6 in AutoCAD.
2. **Open** the first drawing and *click* on **Copy Link** (**Copy View** in Release 13) in the **Edit** menu.
3. **Open** a new document in **PageMaker** and *click* on the **Paste** tool in its **Edit** menu.
4. Repeat steps 2 and 3 for each drawing.

The result is shown in Fig. 15.7.

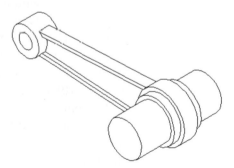

Fig. 15.6 Isometric drawing of the conrod

Note

1. When a drawing or other object is embedded into an AutoCAD drawing (or a document in another application), changes made in the original drawing or object do not affect the embedded drawing or object.

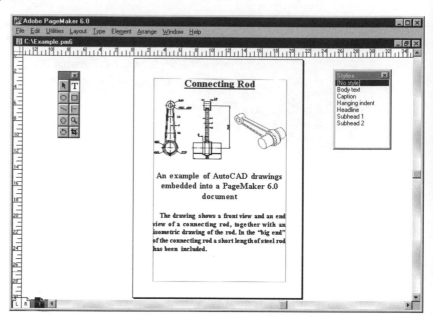

Fig. 15.7 Two linked
drawings in a **PageMaker**
document

2. When a drawing or other object is linked within another application any change made in the original object is reflected in the linked object.
3. Try using the tool **Cut** from the **Edit** menu. As its name implies it will cut part of a drawing for pasting into another application.

Exercises

1. Figure 15.8 shows a drawing which has been inserted into a Windows **Write** document, with text added using the word-processing capability of Write. Open any drawing you may have on disk and link it with a **Write** document and add suitable text.
2. Figure 15.9 shows a **Write** document with text explaining the method by which the text was linked to an AutoCAD drawing (Fig. 15.10). Open any drawing you may have saved in AutoCAD. Enter some suitable text in a **Write** document and either embed or link the text into the AutoCAD drawing. Figure 15.10 shows an example of such text being embedded or linked to an AutoCAD drawing.
3. Enter some text into a **Write** document. Save the text to a suitable filename. Link the text, pasting it into the AutoCAD drawing. Save the drawing. Then open the **Write** document and alter the text. Save the **Write** document to its original filename. Open the AutoCAD drawing and check whether the text changes have taken place in the drawing.

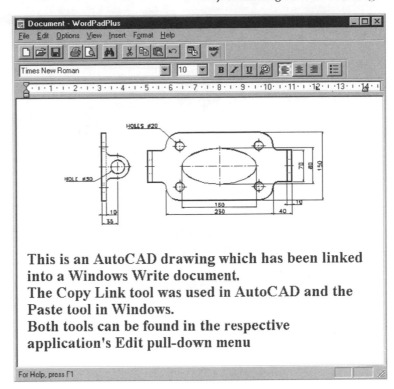

Fig. 15.8 Exercise 1

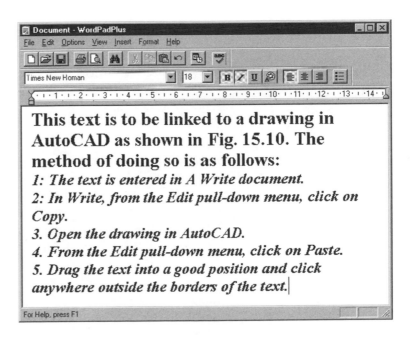

Fig. 15.9 Exercise 2 – text in a **WordPad** document

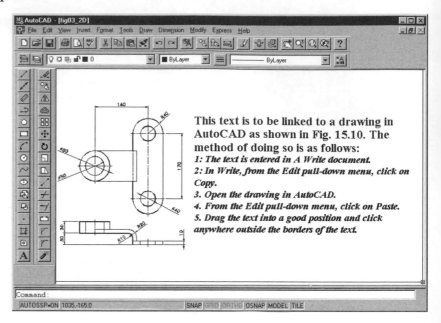

Fig. 15.10 Exercise 2 – the
text linked or embedded in
an AutoCAD drawing

CHAPTER 16

3D surfaces

Note on AutoCAD LT

From this chapter onwards, the examples and exercises cannot be worked in any release of AutoCAD LT because AutoCAD LT has only very limited 3D capability. 3D drawings constructed in AutoCAD can be opened in AutoCAD LT but only very limited editing can be done.

The AutoCAD 3D coordinate system

So far we have been dealing with constructions in 2D (two dimensions), in which points on screen can be selected or *entered* in terms of X,Y coordinate points. When constructing any drawing in 3D (three-dimensions) a third coordinate (the Z coordinate) is required.

In AutoCAD the X coordinate is horizontal (on screen), the Y coordinate is vertical, and the Z coordinate is perpendicular (at right angles) to the surface of the screen. The Z coordinate is positive in the direction out of the screen (that is towards the operator) and negative into the screen (away from the operator).

Taking the example of the simple support stand shown in Fig. 16.1, a pictorial view of the 3D support stand 'within' the screen is shown in Fig. 16.2. The coordinates are shown in their positive directions.

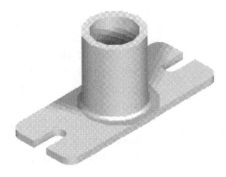

Fig. 16.1 Rendering of a support bracket

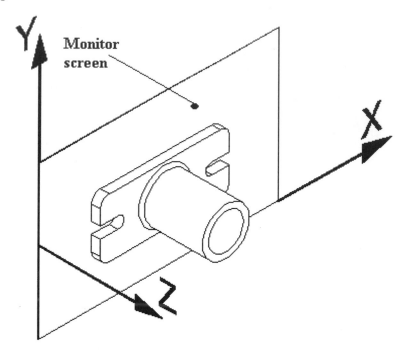

Fig. 16.2 A pictorial view of the *x,y,z* axes

3D surfaces and solids

As the name implies, when constructing 3D model drawings using the **3D Surfaces** tools, only the surfaces of the model are constructed. If such a model is cut in half on screen, then its interior will appear empty. However, if a 3D model constructed with the aid of the **Solids** tools were cut in half, a new surface forms along the cut, i.e. the model behaves as if it were solid.

The **3D Surfaces** tools are common to all releases of AutoCAD from Release 10 onwards, the only differences is that from Release 13 onwards the tools are also available in toolbars.

The Surfaces tools

Fig. 16.3 **Surfaces** toolbar (Releases 13 and 14/AutoCAD 2000)

Figure 16.3 shows the names of the tools in the **Surfaces** toolbar. This toolbar is common to Releases 13 and 14, and AutoCAD 2000. Note the first icon is the **2D Solid** tool which is not a 3D tool.

Any of the tools can be called from the toolbar, but it is probably quicker to call them from the **3D Objects** dialog box (Fig. 16.4) brought on screen by *clicking* on **3D Surfaces . . . (3D Objects . . .** in some releases) in the **Surfaces** sub-menu in the **Draw** menu (Fig. 16.5). A *double-click* on the name of the tool in the dialog box list, or in the box containing its icon, is sufficient to bring the tool into action at the command line.

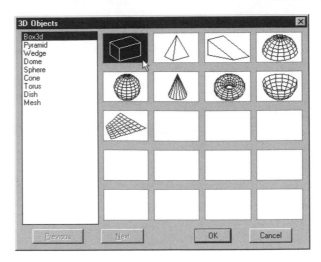

Fig. 16.4 **3D Objects** dialog box

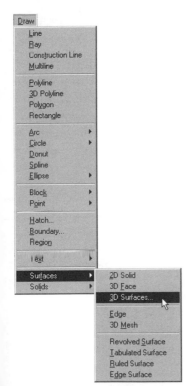

Fig. 16.5 Calling the **3D Objects** dialog box

Notes

1. The **3D Objects** dialog box is common to all the releases described in this book.
2. 3D models constructed with the **Surfaces** tools are of value in some situations, but it is the **Solids** tools which will prove to be more frequently used in connection with the construction of 3D models. Therefore the examples given in this chapter are of a very simple nature, but sufficient to demonstrate how each of the tools are used.

Viewing 3D solid model drawings

The 'user coordinate system' (**UCS**) allows the operator to place a 3D model in any plane other than that commonly used when constructing 2D drawings.

So far we have been using what is known as the 'world coordinate system' (**WCS**). If a 3D model drawing is built in the WCS, the model can be viewed from any other direction by using one of two 3D systems: the **UCS** or **3D Views** (Release 14 and AutoCAD 2000 only), or the **Vpoint** command (all releases).

Note

Although a 3D model can be viewed using any of the three systems (**UCS**, **3D Views** or **Vpoint**), it is only in the **UCS** that 3D constructions can be added to a model. In either **3D Views** or **Vpoints** any constructions added are created as if drawn in the **WCS**.

The UCS presets

The quickest way of placing a 3D model in a new **UCS** is to call the **UCS Orientation** dialog box (**Orthographic UCS** in AutoCAD 2000) and *clicking* in or on the desired viewing position (Fig. 16.6). The dialog box is called to screen from the menus indicated in Fig. 16.6.

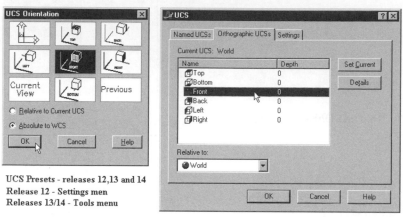

UCS Presets - releases 12,13 and 14
Release 12 - Settings men
Releases 13/14 - Tools menu

Fig. 16.6 **UCS Presets**

UCS Presets AutoCAD 2000 – Tools menu

Figure 16.7 shows a rendering of a 3D model drawing constructed in AutoCAD. Figure 16.8 shows each of the six positions of the **UCS Presets** or the **Orthographic UCS** viewing positions.

Fig. 16.7 Rendering of a 3D solid model drawing

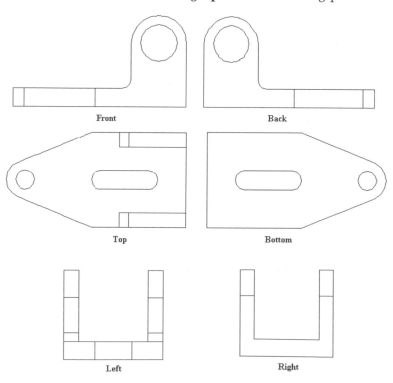

Fig. 16.8 **UCS** preset viewing positions of the model in Fig. 16.7

The set variable UCSFOLLOW

The UCS cannot be changed unless the set variable **UCSFOLLOW** is set 'on' (that is, to 1) as follows:

Command: *enter* ucsfollow *right-click*
Enter new value for UCSFOLLOW <0>: *enter* 1 *right-click*
Command:

3D Views

Call either the **Vpoint** tool (any of the releases), or **3D Views** from the **View** menu in Release 14 and AutoCAD 2000 (Fig. 16.9). Figure 16.10 shows the different pictorial views possible using the **Isometric** tools from the **View** menu of Release 14 or AutoCAD 2000. The **Vpoint** positions are indicated in Fig. 16.10.

To call **Vpoint**:

Command: *enter* vpoint *right-click*
Rotate/<View point>: *enter* -1,-1,1 *right-click*
Regenerating drawing
Command:

Fig. 16.9 **Isometric** views in the **View** menu

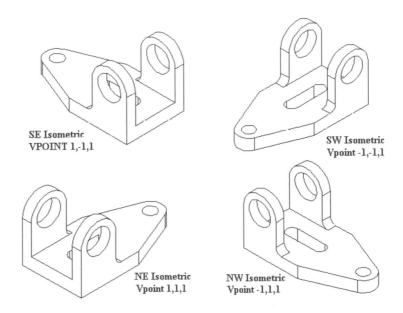

SE Isometric
VPOINT 1,-1,1

SW Isometric
Vpoint -1,-1,1

NE Isometric
Vpoint 1,1,1

NW Isometric
Vpoint -1,1,1

Fig. 16.10 **3D Views** and the corresponding **Vpoint** views

The 3D model drawing assumes the 'SW isometric' view (see Fig. 16.11).

Note

Although the **Vpoint** tool can be of good use when attempting to place a 3D model in a required viewing position, for general use it is probably easier to use the **3D Views** tools (these are only available in Release 14 and AutoCAD 2000). **Vpoint** is however available in all the releases.

Drawing with the Surfaces tools

Example 1: box (Fig. 16.11)

Double-click on the name **Box** in the **3D Objects** dialog box (Fig. 16.4):

Command:_ai_box
Corner point of box: 60,130
Length: 100
Width: 80
Height: 120
Rotation angle about Z axis: 0
Command: vpoint
Rotate/<Vpoint>: -1,-1,1
Command: hide
Regenerating drawing:
Command:

Example 2: wedge (Fig. 16.11)

Double-click on the name **Wedge** in the **3D Objects** dialog box:

Command:_ai_wedge
Corner of wedge: 205,130

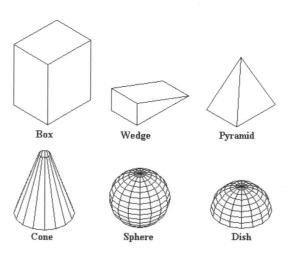

Fig. 16.11 3D objects drawn with **Surfaces** tools

Length: 120
Width: 60
Height: 45
Rotation angle about Z axis: 0
Command: vpoint
Rotate/<Vpoint>: -1,-1,1
Command: hide
Regenerating drawing:
Command:

Example 3: pyramid (Fig. 16.11)

Double-click on the name **Pyramid** in the **3D Objects** dialog box:

Command:_ai_pyramid
First base point: 360,130
Second base point: 450,130
Third base point: 450,200
Fourth base point: 360,200
Ridge/Top/<Apex point>: 405,165,100
Command: vpoint
Rotate/<Vpoint>: -1,-1,1
Command: hide
Regenerating drawing:
Command:

Example 4: cone (Fig. 16.11)

Double-click on the name **Cone** in the **3D Objects** dialog box:

Command:_ai_cone
Base center point: 100,50
Diameter/<Radius> of base: 50
Diameter/<Radius> of top: 10
Height: 120
Number of segments<16>: *right-click*
Command:
Command: vpoint
Rotate/<Vpoint>: -1,-1,1
Command: hide
Regenerating drawing:
Command:

Example 5: sphere (Fig. 16.11)

Double-click on the name **Sphere** in the **3D Objects** dialog box:

Command:_ai_sphere
Center of sphere: 260,50

Diameter/<Radius>: 50
Number of longitudinal segments <16>: *right-click*
Number of latitudinal segments<16>: *right-click*
Command: vpoint
Rotate/<Vpoint>: -1,-1,1
Command: hide
Regenerating drawing:
Command:

Example 6: dome (Fig. 16.11)

Double-click on the name **Dome** in the **3D Objects** dialog box:

Command:_ai_dome
Center of dome: 405,50
Diameter/<Radius>: 50
Number of longitudinal segments<16>: *right-click*
Number of latitudinal segments<16>: *right-click*
Command: vpoint
Rotate/<Vpoint>: -1,-1,1
Command: hide
Regenerating drawing:
Command:

Other Surfaces tools

Other **Surfaces** tools may be called by *clicking* on their names in the **Surfaces** sub-menu of the **Draw** menu (Fig. 16.12). In Releases 13 onwards the tools can be called by *clicking* the appropriate tool icons in the **Surfaces** toolbar (see Fig. 16.3). Alternatively, in any of the releases, the names of the tools as shown below can be *entered* at the command line.

Example 1: 3dface (Fig. 16.14)

Select the tool from the **Draw** menu, *click* on its tool icon in the **Surfaces** toolbar, or *enter* **3dface** at the command line (Fig. 16.13).

Command:_3dface First point: 130,230
Second point: 260,230,100
Third point: 260,120,50
Fourth point: 130,120,150
Third point: *right-click*
Command:

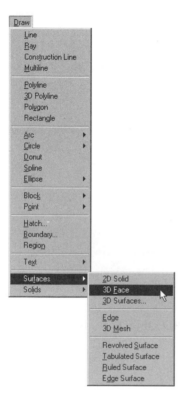

Fig. 16.12 **Surfaces** sub-menu of the **Draw** menu

Fig. 16.13 Calling the **3dface** tool

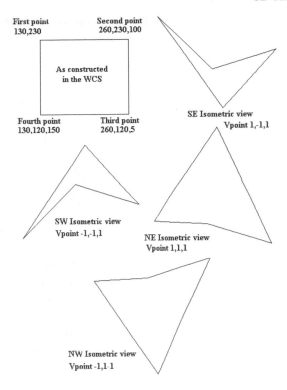

Fig. 16.14 Example 1

Example 2: 3dface (Fig. 16.15)

1. Construct a box: corner of box: 90,260; length 200; width 150; height 30.
2. Construct a 3dface: first point: 60,170,50; second point: 360,170,50; third point: 360,120,50; fourth point: 60,120,50.

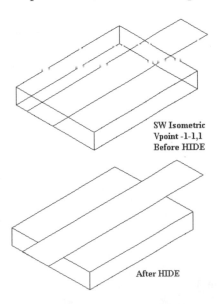

Fig. 16.15 Example 2

3. Place in the **SW Isometric** view (upper drawing Fig. 16.15).
4. Call **Hide** (lower drawing Fig. 16.15).

Note

As can be seen from the lower illustration in Fig. 16.15, the fact that part of the box is hidden behind the 3dface shows that a 3dface is a solid face − it is, what is known as a 3D mesh surface.

Example 3: 3dface (Fig. 16.16)

Construct 3dfaces as follows:

Command:_3dface First point: 100,210
Second point: 100,70
Third point: 100,70,100
Fourth point: 100,210,100
Third point: 300,210
Fourth point: 300,70
Third point: 100,70,100
Fourth point: 100,210,100
Third point: 100,210
Fourth point: 100,70
Third point: 300,70
Fourth point: 300,210
Third point: *right-click*
Command:

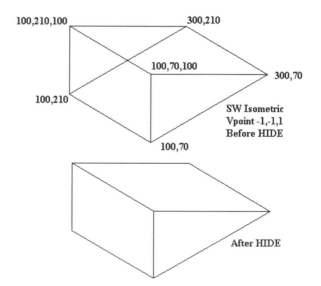

Fig. 16.16 Example 3

Note

Note the continuity between the third and fourth points. A complex structure of 3dfaces can be built up in this manner.

Example 4: edgesurf (Fig. 16.18)

1. Set **UCSFOLLOW** to 1.
2. Place in **Right UCS** (from the **UCS Presets**).
3. **Zoom** to 1.
4. Draw an arc from 50,0 to 170,60 to 340,0.
5. Place in the **World UCS**.
6. Zoom to 1.
7. **Copy** the arc through 200 vertically.
8. Draw a pline from 50,0 to 50,200 and another from 340,0 to 340,200.
9. Place in the **SW Isometric** view.
10. At the command line:

    Command: *enter* surftab1 *right-click*
    New value for SURTAB1<6>: *enter* 16 *right-click*
    Command: *enter* surftab2 *right-click*
    New value for SURTAB2<6>: *enter* 16 *right-click*
    Command:

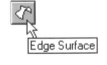

Edge Surface

Edgesurf

Fig. 16.17 Calling the **Edgesurf** tool

11. Call **Edgesurf** (Fig. 16.17):

    Command:_edgesurf
    Select edge 1: *pick* one of the objects
    Select edge 2: *pick* another adjacent object
    Select edge 3: *pick* another adjacent object
    Select edge 4: *pick* the last object
    Command:

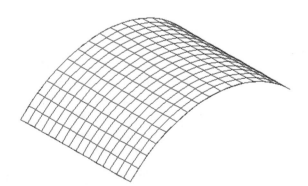

Fig. 16.18 **Edgesurf** example

Revsurf

Fig. 16.19 Calling the
Revsurf tool

Note

1. The two set variables **SURFTAB1** and **SURFTAB2** set the size of the meshes for surfaces in both directions. The way in which the two settings affect a surface mesh can be checked by changing the variables and using **Edgesurf** again on the four objects.

2. If the four objects in an edgesurf outline do not touch at their ends, the surface does not form.

3. Note the use of **UCS** and **3D View** during the construction of this simple mesh.

Example 5: revsurf (Fig. 16.22)

1. With the aid of the **Pline** tool construct the outline Fig. 16.20. There are two separate parts to this drawing as shown in Fig. 16.21: a path curve and an axis of revolution.

2. Set **SURFTAB1** to 24 and **SURFTAB2** to 16.

3. Call **Revsurf** (Fig. 16.20):

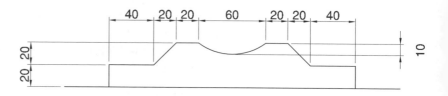

Fig. 16.20 **Revsurf** example

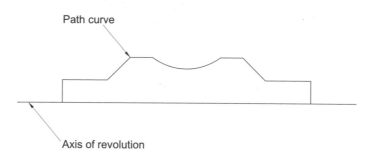

Fig. 16.21 **Revsurf** example –
the path curve and the axis
of revolution

Command:_revsurf
Select path curve: *pick* the curve
Select axis of revolution: *pick* the axis of revolution
Start angle <0>: *right-click*
Included angle (+=ccw, -=cw) <Full circle>: *right-click*
Command:

The surface of revolution forms (Fig. 16.22).

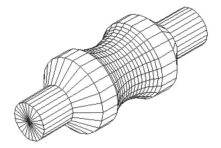

Fig. 16.22 **Revsurf** example

Tabulated Surface

Tabsurf

Fig. 16.23 Calling the
Tabsurf tool

Example 6: tabsurf (Fig. 16.25)

1. Construct the pline outline in Fig. 16.24.
2. With **Line** draw a line from 180,160 to 180,160,150 (see Fig. 16.25).
3. Place the screen in the **SW Isometric** view.
4. Call **Tabsurf** (Fig. 16.23):

Command:_tabsurf
Select path curve: *pick*
Select direction vector: *pick*
Command:

The tabsurf forms (Fig. 16.25).

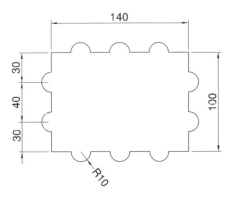

Fig. 16.24 **Tabsurf** example –
example path curve

Note

1. When selecting the direction vector, take care with the position along the vector at which *picking* takes place. *Pick* low and the tabsurf forms as shown in Fig. 16.25. *Pick* high and the tabsurf forms below the direction vector.
2. The direction vector can be at an angle to the **WCS** as illustrated in Fig. 16.26.

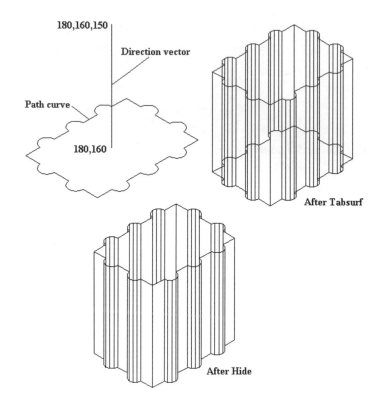

Fig. 16.25 **Tabsurf** example

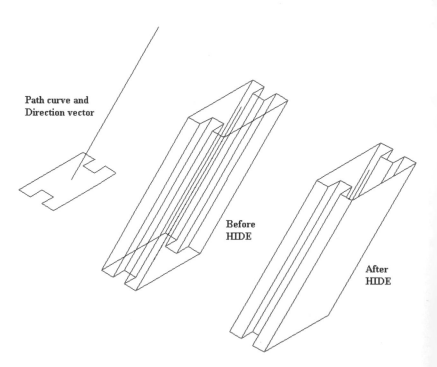

Fig. 16.26 The direction vector can be at an angle to **WCS**

Example 7: rulesurf (Fig. 16.29)

1. Place in **Right UCS**.
2. **Zoom** to 1.
3. Construct the polyline outline in Fig. 16.27.
4. Call the **World UCS**.
5. **Copy** the pline 300 to the right.
6. Place in the **SW Isometric** view.
7. Set **SURFTAB1** to 32.
8. Call **Rulesurf** (Fig. 16.28):

Command:_rulesurf
Select first defining curve: *pick* one of the plines
Select second defining curve: *pick* the other pline
Command:

The resulting rulesurf is illustrated in the upper drawing of Fig. 16.29.

190
50
R45
10

Fig. 16.27 Example path curve for **Rulesurf**

Ruled Surface
Rulesurf

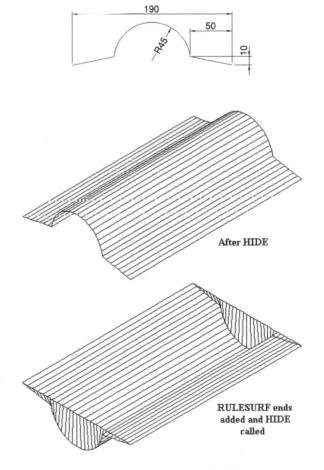

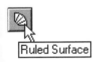

Fig. 16.28 Calling the **Rulesurf** tool

After HIDE
RULESURF ends added and HIDE called

Fig. 16.29 **Rulesurf** example

Note

The lower of the two drawings in Fig. 16.29 shows the ends of the rulesurf filled in with two further rulesurfs. This was made possible by adding more defining curves (straight lines) between the lower ends of original defining curves for the main surface. Each end must be treated separately.

Further examples

Figure 16.30 shows examples of the use of **tabsurf**. Figure 16.31 shows an example of the use of **Revsurf**. Figure 16.32 shows an example of the use of **Edgesurf**. Figures 16.33–16.34 show yet another example of a 3D surfaces model constructed with the aid of **Edgesurf**.

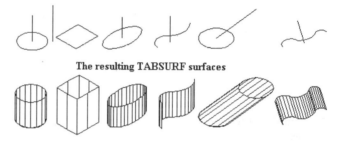

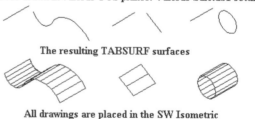

Fig. 16.30 **Tabsurf** examples

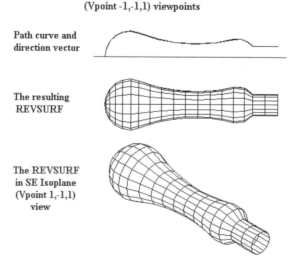

Fig. 16.31 **Revsurf** example

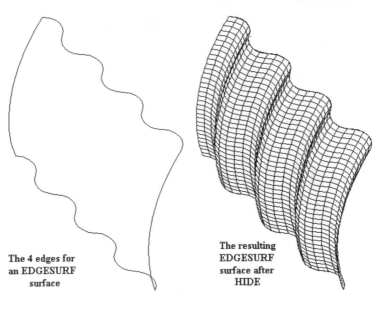

The 4 edges for an EDGESURF surface

The resulting EDGESURF surface after HIDE

Fig. 16.32 **Edgesurf** example

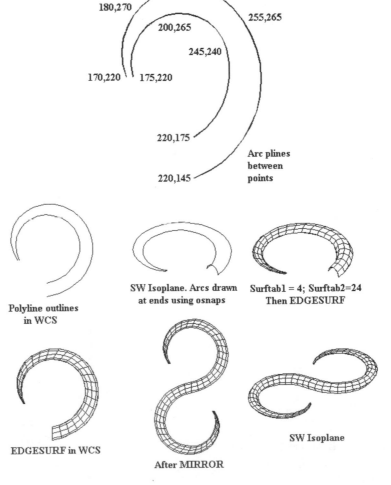

180,270

200,265

255,265

245,240

170,220   175,220

220,175

Arc plines between points

220,145

Fig. 16.33 **Edgesurf** example – points on the two curves for edges of the surface

Polyline outlines in WCS

SW Isoplane. Arcs drawn at ends using osnaps

Surftab1 = 4; Surftab2=24 Then EDGESURF

EDGESURF in WCS

After MIRROR

SW Isoplane

Fig. 16.34 **Edgesurf** example – stages in constructing the model

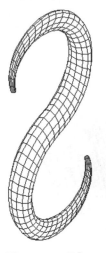

Question

What is the purpose of the two set variables **SURFTAB1** and **SURFTAB2**?

Exercises

1. Figure 16.36 is a dimensioned drawing of the path curve for a tabsurf surface standing 120 high. Figure 16.37 shows the tabsurf surface which is topped with a rulesurf surface made from two defining curves created by first copying the tabsurf curve path and then breaking the outline into two equal parts. Construct the surfaces shown in Fig. 16.38 to the given sizes.

Fig. 16.35 **Edgesurf** example – the final model

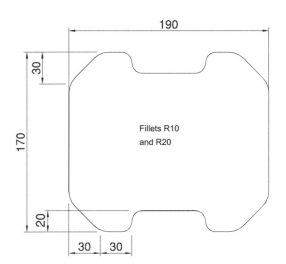

Fillets R10 and R20

Fig. 16.36 Exercise 1 – path curve

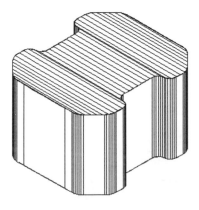

Fig. 16.37 Exercise 1

2. Figure 16.38 is the end view of the 300 unit length of moulding constructed from surfaces shown in Fig. 16.39. Construct the surfaces to the dimensions given in the Figs 16.38 and 16.39.

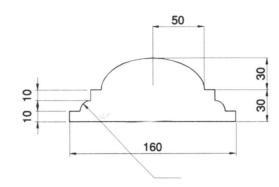

Fig. 16.38 Exercise 2 – dimensions of end view

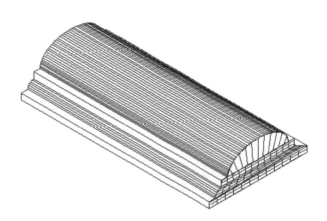

Fig. 16.39 Exercise 2

3. Figure 16.40 is a revolved surface constructed from the path curve and axis of revolution shown in Fig. 16.41. Construct the surface of revolution to the given sizes.

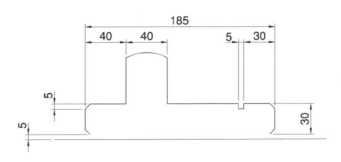

Fig. 16.40 Exercise 3 – path curve and axis of evolution

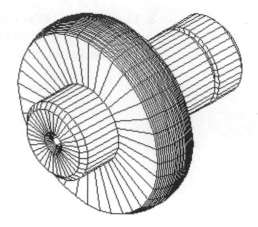

Fig. 16.41 Exercise 3

4. Figure 16.42 shows a dimensioned front view and plan for the 3D surfaces model shown to the right of the front view and plan. Working to the given dimensions construct the 3D surfaces model.

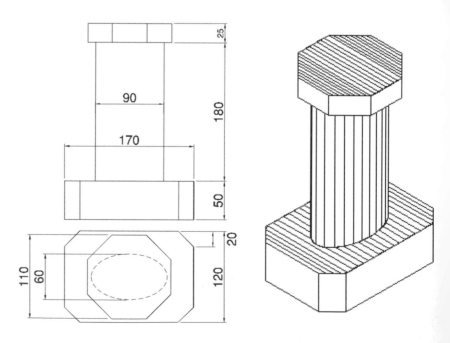

Fig. 16.42 Exercise 4

5. Figure 16.43 shows a dimensioned front view and plan of the path curve and axis of revolution for the surface of revolution pictured to the right of the front view and plan. Working to the given sizes, construct the surface of revolution.

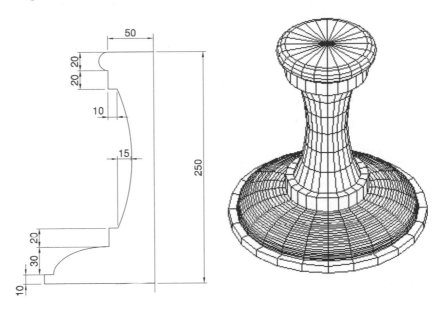

Fig. 16.43 Exercise 5

CHAPTER 17

3D solids

Introduction

The construction of 3D model drawings in AutoCAD began with the introduction of the Advanced Modeling Extension (AME) software with Release 11. It was necessary to add the extension software when Release 12 for Windows was introduced, but with subsequent releases the capability to construct 3D solids was incorporated within AutoCAD and the AME software was no longer required.

In effect, whether using Release 12 (with AME loaded as an extra) or later releases, the construction of 3D solid model drawings is identical throughout the releases under consideration here. There are slight differences in appearance of the solids when constructed in Release 12 compared with later releases, but this does not prevent the methods described in this chapter from being used with any of the releases.

Solids tools

The construction of 3D solid models involves a number of tools:

1. To create the basic solids from which models can be built up: **Box**, **Sphere**, **Wedge**, **Cone**, **Cylinder**, **Torus**.
2. To **Extrude** or **Revolve** 3D solids from outlines.
3. To **Union**, **Subtract** or **Intersect** 3D models.
4. To **Slice** and/or **Section** models created from unions, subtractions or intersections.

The methods of calling these tools varies between the releases under consideration here. Figures 17.1–17.4 show the tools in the toolbars, menus and sub-menus from the various releases. Remember no matter which release is in use, the creation of 3D solid model drawings is largely the same.

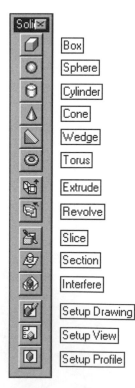

Fig. 17.1 **Solids** toolbar (Releases 13 and 14/AutoCAD 2000)

Fig. 17.2 **Modify II** toolbar
showing the Boolean
operatives

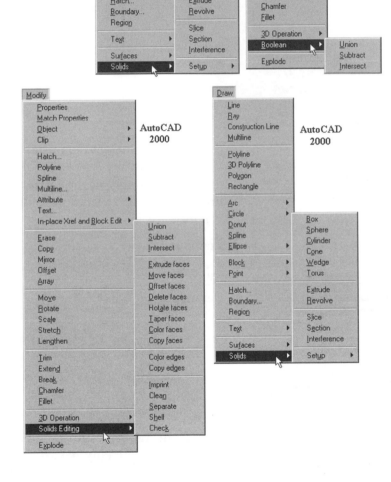

Fig. 17.3 Menus and
sub-menus from which the
Solids tools can be selected
(various releases)

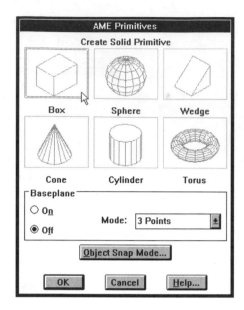

Fig. 17.4 **AME Primitives**
dialog box (Release 12)

Note

Although the **Surfaces** tools have similar names to the **Solids** tools,
calling the tools by *entering* tool names at the command line is different. To call any of the **Surfaces** tools by *entry* at the Command
line **ai_** must be *entered* preceding the name. To call the **Surfaces**
sphere:

Command: *enter* ai_sphere *right-click*

Whereas to call a **Solids** sphere:

Command: *enter* sphere *right-click*

Examples of 3D models created with Solids tools

Example 1: Box and Subtract (Fig. 17.7)

1. Call **Box**: in Release 12 *click* on its icon in the **AME Primitives**
dialog box; in other releases *click* on its icon in the **Solids** toolbar,
click on its name in the appropriate menu, or *enter* **box** at the
command line (any release) – see Fig. 17.5.

Command:_box
Center/<Corner of box>: 130,220
Cube/Length/<Other corner>: 340,120
Height: 120
Command: *right-click*

Fig. 17.5 Calling the **Box** tool

BOX
Center/<Corner of box>: 150,220,20
Cube/Length/<Other corner>: 320,120,20
Height: 100
Command:

2. Place in the **SW Isometric** view (Fig. 17.7).
3. Call **Subtract**: in releases other than Release 12, *click* on its icon in the **Modify II** toolbar, *click* on its name in the appropriate menu, or *enter* **subtract** at the command line (any release). See Fig. 17.6.

Command:_subtract
Select objects: *pick* the larger box **1 found**
Select objects: *right-click*
Select objects and regions to subtract . . .
Select objects: *pick* the other box **1 found**
Select objects: *right-click*
Command:

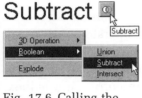

Subtract

Fig. 17.6 Calling the
Subtract tool

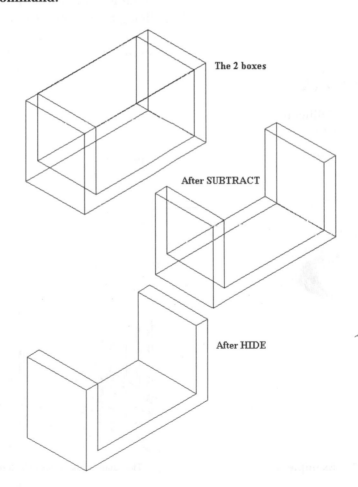

The 2 boxes

After SUBTRACT

After HIDE

Fig. 17.7 Example 1

The inner box is subtracted from the larger. See the central illustration in Fig. 17.7.

4. Call **Hide**: the 3D solid drawing appears as in the lower illustration of Fig. 17.7.

Notes

1. The three tools **Union, Subtract**, and **Intersection** are known as the three **Boolean** operators. The Boolean operators only work on objects created with **Solids** tools.
2. If *entering* **Solids** tool names in Release 12 at the command line the prefix **sol** must be included in the *entry* – e.g. **solbox**, **solcone** etc.

Example 2: Cylinder and Union (Fig. 17.9)

1. Call **Cylinder**: in Release 12 *click* on its icon in the **AME Primitives** dialog box; in other releases *click* on its icon in the **Solids** toolbar, *click* on its name in the appropriate menu (Fig. 17.5), or *enter* **cylinder** at the command line – see Fig. 17.8.

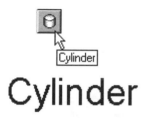

Cylinder

Fig. 17.8 Calling the **Cylinder** tool

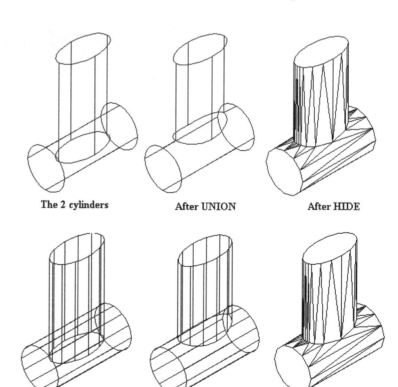

The 2 cylinders   After UNION   After HIDE

Fig. 17.9 Example 2   The same solids as above with the variable ISOLINES set to 12

Command:_cylinder
Elliptical/<Center point>: e
Center of ellipse/<Axis endpoint>: c
Center of ellipse <0,0,0>: 220,160
Axis endpoint: 260,160
Other axis endpoint: 220,140
Center at other end/<Height>: 140
Command:

2. Place in **UCS Right**.
3. **Zoom** to 1.
4. Call **Cylinder**:

Command:_cylinder
Elliptical/<Center point>: 160,0
Diameter/<Radius>: 30
Center at other end/<Height>: 120
Command:

5. Place in the **WCS**.
6. With the aid of **Move**, move the circular cylinder to be central to the elliptical cylinder.
7. Place in the **SW Isometric** view.
8. Call **Union** (see Fig. 17.6):

Command:_union
Select objects: *pick* the elliptical cylinder **1 found**
Select objects: *pick* the circular cylinder **1 found**
Select objects: *right-click*
Command:

9. Call **Hide**.

Note

The number of lines seen as solid primitives that appear on screen is controlled by the set variable **ISOLINES**. The variable is set as follows:

Command: *enter* isolines *right-click*
New value for ISOLINES <4>: 12
Command:

Figure 17.9 shows the differences between setting this variable to 4 and to 12.

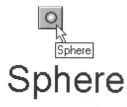

Fig. 17.10 Calling the **Sphere** tool

Sphere

Example 3: Sphere, Cylinder and Box (Fig. 17.11)

1. Set **ISOLINES** to 12.
2. Call **Sphere**: in Release 12 *click* on its icon in the **AME Primitives** dialog box; in other releases *click* on its icon in the **Solids** toolbar, *click* on its name in the appropriate menu (Fig. 17.5), or *enter* **sphere** at the command line – see Fig. 17.10.

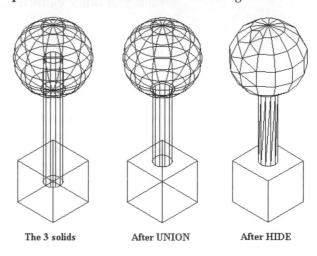

The 3 solids   After UNION   After HIDE

Fig. 17.11 Example 3

Command_sphere
Center of sphere <0,0,0>: 240,170
Diameter/<Radius>: 40
Command: cylinder
CYLINDER
Elliptical/<Center point>: 240,170
Diameter/<Radius>: 10
Center at other end/<Height>: c
Center at other end: 240,170,150
Command: box
Center/<Corner of box>: c
Cube/Length/<Center of box>: 240,170
Length: 50
Command:

2. Place in **SW Isometric** view.
3. Call **Union** and union the three solids together.

Example 4: Cone, Wedge and Intersect (Fig. 17.14)

1. Call **Cone**: in Release 12 *click* on its icon in the **AME Primitives** dialog box; in other releases *click* on its icon in the **Solids** toolbar, *click* on its name in the appropriate menu (Fig. 17.5), or *enter* **cone** at the command line – see Fig. 17.12.

Cone

Fig. 17.12 Calling the **Cone** tool

Command:_cone
Elliptical/<Center point>: 230,160
Diameter/<Radius>: 60
Apex/<Height>: 160
Command:

2. Call **Wedge**: in Release 12 *click* on its icon in the **AME Primitives** dialog box; in other releases *click* on its icon in the **Solids** toolbar, *click* on its name in the appropriate menu (Fig. 17.5), or *enter* **wedge** at the command line – see Fig. 17.13.

Command:_wedge
Center/<Corner of wedge>: 170,220
Cube/Length/<Other corner>: 290,100
Height: 60
Command:

3. Call **Intersect** – see Fig. 17.6.

Command:_intersect
Select objects: *pick* the cone **1 found**
Select objects: *pick* the wedge **1 found**
Select objects: *right-click*
Command:

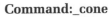

Wedge

Fig. 17.13 Calling the **Wedge** tool

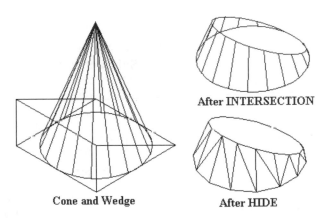

Cone and Wedge

After INTERSECTION

After HIDE

Fig. 17.14 Example 4

Example 5: Extrude and Subtract (Fig. 17.17)

1. Construct the pline outline shown in Fig. 17.15.
2. Call **Extrude**: in Release 12 *click* on its name in the **Model** menu; in other releases *click* on its icon in the **Solids** toolbar, *click* on its name in the appropriate menu (Fig. 17.5), or *enter* **extrude** or **ext** at the command line (any release) – see Fig. 17.16.

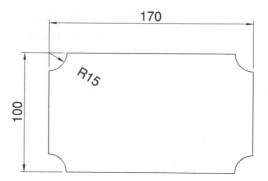

Fig. 17.15 Example 5 – pline outline

Ext

Fig. 17.16 Calling the **Extrude** tool

Command:_extrude
Select objects: *pick* the pline **1 found**
Select objects: *right-click*
Path/<Height of extrusion>: 50
Extrusion taper angle <0>: *right-click*
Command:

3. Call **Cylinder:**

Command:_cylinder
Elliptical/<Center point>: 140,150
Diameter/<Radius>: 15
Center at other end/<Height>: 50
Command:

4. Repeat item 3 at points 250,150; 250,185; 140,185.
5. Place in **SW Isometric** view.
6. Call **Subtract** and subtract the cylinders from the extrusion.

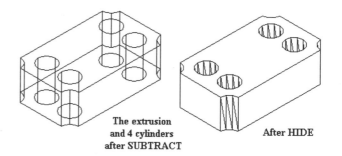

The extrusion
and 4 cylinders
after SUBTRACT

After HIDE

Fig. 17.17 Example 5 – **Extrude** and **Subtract**

Example 6: Revolve and Union (Fig. 17.21)

1. Place in **UCS Front**.
2. **Zoom** to 1.
3. With the aid of the **Polyline** and **offset** tools construct the outline described in Fig. 17.18. Make sure the outline, including the offset and the plines closing the offsets at both ends, is a closed pline.

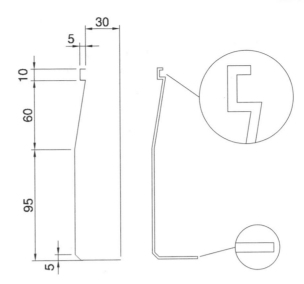

Fig. 17.18 Example 6 – pline outline

Rev

Fig. 17.19 Calling the **Revolve** tool

4. Set **ISOLINES** to 32.
5. Call **Revolve**: in releases other than Release 12, *click* on its icon in the **Solids** toolbar, *click* on its name in the appropriate menu (Fig. 17.5), or *enter* **revolve** or **rev** at the command line – see Fig. 17.19.

Command:_revolve
Select objects: *pick* the closed pline
Axis of revolution – Object/X/Y/<Start point of axis>: *pick* as shown in Fig. 17.20
<End point of axis>: *pick*
Angle of revolution<full circle>: *right-click*
Command: and the solid of revolution forms

5. Place in **SW Isometric** view.
6. Call **Hide**.

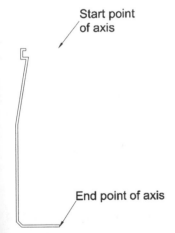

Fig. 17.20 Example 6 – ends of axis

Fig. 17.21 Example 6 – **Revolve** and **Hide**

Before HIDE   After HIDE

Example 7: a 3D solid model (Figs 17.22–17.25)

1. Working to the dimensions given in Fig. 17.22 and with the aid of the **Polyline** tool, construct the outlines shown in Fig. 17.23.

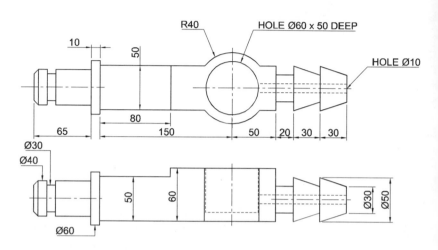

Fig. 17.22 Example 7 – front view and plan

Fig. 17.23 Example 7 – outlines ready for **Extrude** and **Revolve**

2. Set **ISOLINES** to 12.
3. Figure 17.24 top drawing: with **Extrude** and **Revolve**, extrude or revolve the four parts as shown.
4. Place in **UCS Front**.
5. With the aid of the **Move** tool, move the parts into their correct positions relative to each other.
6. Place in the **SW Isometric** view.
7. With the aid of the **Union** tool, union the four parts together.
8. Place in the **UCS Right** and with **Cylinder** create a cylinder 110 long, radius 5 central to the right-hand end of the 3D solid.
9. Place in the **WCS** and move the cylinder just formed into its correct position.
10. With **Subtract**, subtract the cylinder from the 3D solid model.
11. Place in the **NE Isometric** view; call **Hide** (Fig. 17.25).

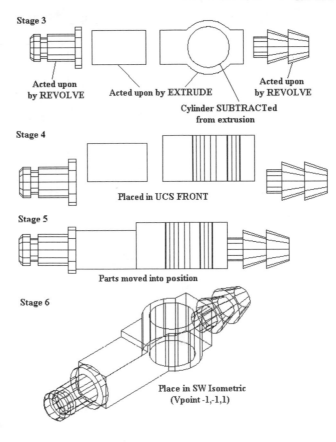

Fig. 17.24 Example 7 – stages in the construction of the 3D model

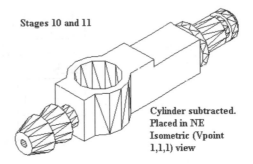

Fig. 17.25 Example 7 – the completed 3D model after **Hide**

Example 8: a 3D solid model (Figs 17.25–17.27)

Figure 17.26 is a dimensioned front view and plan of the model to be constructed.

1. Construct two closed plines as shown in Stage 1 of Fig. 17.27. With **Extrude**, extrude the left-hand pline by 15 and the right-hand pline by 30.

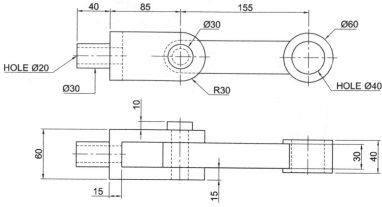

Fig. 17.26 Example 8 –
dimensions

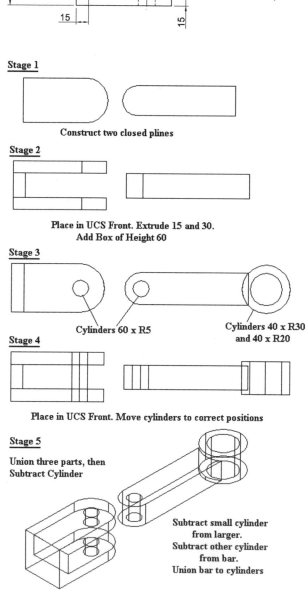

Fig. 17.27 Example 8 – stages
1–5

2. Place in the **Front UCS**. With **Move**, move the extrusions to their correct positions in relation to each other as shown in Stage 2 of Fig. 17.27. Construct a **Box** of height 60 as shown. It may be necessary to place the model in the **WCS** to move the box into its correct position.

3. In the **WCS** construct cylinders as shown as Stage 3 in Fig. 17.27.

4. Go back to the **Front UCS** and move the cylinders to their correct positions as shown in Stage 4 of Fig. 17.27.

5. Place the model so far constructed in **SW Isometric** view.

6. With **Union**, union the three parts of the left-hand model together.

7. With **Subtract**, subtract the cylinder from this union.

8. With **Subtract**, subtract the R20 cylinder from the R30 cylinder.

9. With **Union**, union the two cylinders to the bar.

10. In the **WCS** construct two cylinders one of R10 and height 60, the other of R15 and height 10. Go back into the **Front UCS** and move the cylinder to their correct positions. Then with **Union**, union the two cylinders to form the pin holding the two parts of the model together.

11. Place in the **NE Isometric** view and the call **Hide** (see Stage 7 of Fig. 17.28).

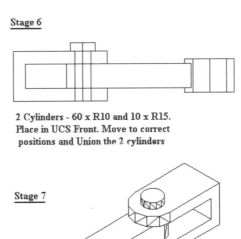

Fig. 17.28 Example 8 – stages 6 and 7

Questions

1. What is the major difference between 3D models created with the aid of the **Surfaces** tools and those created using the **Solids** tools?

2. There are in general two methods of calling the **Solids** tools when using Release 12. Can you state what they are?
3. What is meant by 'Boolean operators'?
4. Why is the **UCS** so important when constructing 3D solid model drawings?
5. Can additions to a 3D solid model drawing be made when in one of the **Isometric** viewing positions?
6. What is the purpose of the set variable **ISOLINES**?
7. What is the purpose of the **Hide** tool?
8. What are the abbreviations for the two tools **Extrude** and **Revolve**?
9. In Example 6 (page 220) in this chapter, the pline was offset and closed before using the **Revolve** tool. Why was this?
10. Have you tried using **Revolve** to form a solid of revolution through 180°? Or through 90°?

Exercises

1. Figure 17.29 shows the 3D solid model drawing which should result from this exercise. Figure 17.30 gives the dimensions in front and end views of the model. Start by constructing a pline outline from which the body of the model can be extruded. Then extrude two further plines for the indents at front and back. Subtract these from the main body. Finally create a cylinder to subtract from the body. Then use **Hide**.

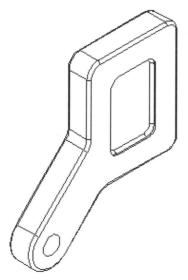

Fig. 17.29 Exercise 1

Fig. 17.30 Exercise 1 – front and end views giving dimensions

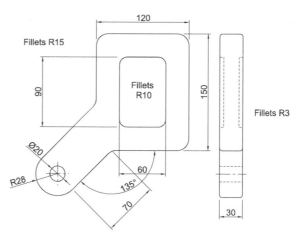

2. Figure 17.31 shows the 3D model for this exercise. It is a simple extrusion to which a box is added to form the tongue on the left-hand end.
3. Figure 17.33 shows a pair of extrusions unioned to each other, with cylinders subtracted to form the holes. Construct the two

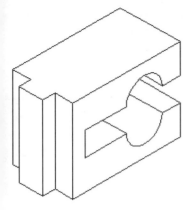

Fig. 17.31 Exercise 2

Fig. 17.32 Exercise 2 –
dimensions

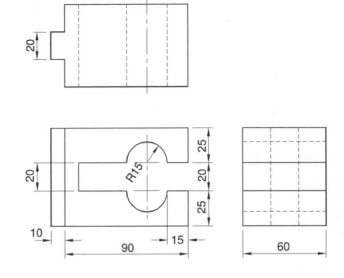

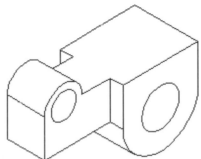
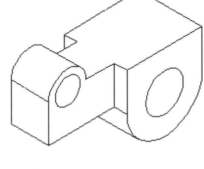
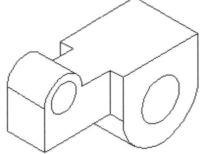

Fig. 17.33 Exercise 3

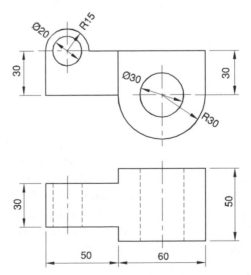

Fig. 17.34 Exercise 3 –
dimensions

plines from which the extrusions are created. Move the left-hand extrusion so that it is central to the left-hand end of the right-hand one. Join the two with **Union**. Then subtract the two cylinders from the resulting union.

4. Figure 17.35 shows a rendered version of the model in this exercise. Figure 17.36 is a dimensioned front view and plan of the model. The main body of the model can be created as a solid of revolution from a pline in the **Front UCS**. The hole is an extrusion created in the **WCS** which is subtracted from the main body. The holes in the base are cylinders subtracted from the main body.

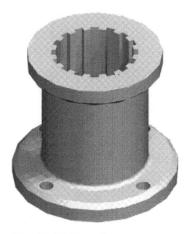

Fig. 17.35 Exercise 4

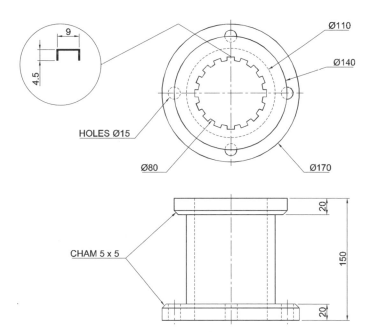

Fig. 17.36 Exercise 4 – dimensioned views

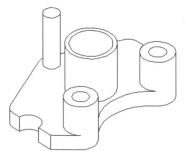

Fig. 17.37 Exercise 5

5. Figure 17.37 shows the 3D model for this exercise and a dimensioned pair of views is given in Fig. 17.38. Start by extruding a pline outline for the base, followed by creating pairs of cylinders, the inner ones of which are subtracted from the outer. Then create a cylinder for the rod at the rear. Finally position the cylinders accurately in their positions and with **Union** join all the parts together.

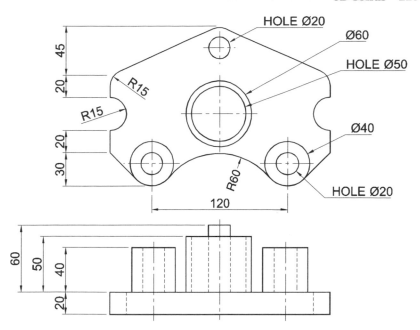

Fig. 17.38 Exercise 5 – dimensioned views

6. Figure 17.39 shows the 3D model for this exercise. The base is a pline from which two cylinders have been subtracted. The arm is an extrusion created in the **Front UCS**. The cylinder with a hole attached to the arm is created from an inner cylinder subtracted from an outer. The three parts are then correctly positioned and joined to each other with **Union**.

7. Figure 17.41 shows a 3D model of an arm from a machine. Figure 17.42 is a dimensioned pair of views of the model. The arm is a simple extrusion created in the **Front UCS** from a pline outline. It is then joined with **Union** to two cylinders, one subtracted from the other.

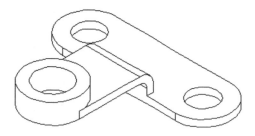

Fig. 17.39 Exercise 6

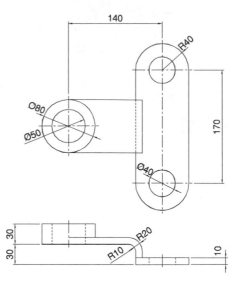

Fig. 17.40 Exercise 6 –
dimensioned views

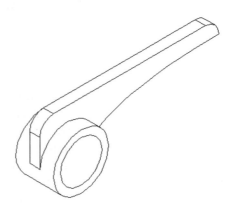

Fig. 17.41 Exercise 7

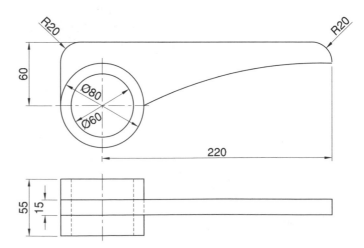

Fig. 17.42 Exercise 7 –
dimensioned views

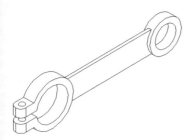

Fig. 17.43 Exercise 8

8. Figure 17.43 shows the 3D model for this exercise and Fig. 17.44 a dimensioned pair of views of the model. A pair of cylinders constructed in the **Front UCS** – one cylinder of each pair subtracted from the other – are joined with **Union** to a box. An extrusion for the lips at the left-hand end is constructed in the **WCS** and joined with **Union** to the other parts of the model.

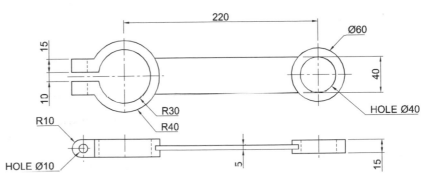

Fig. 17.44 Exercise 8 – dimensioned views

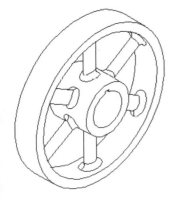

Fig. 17.45 Exercise 9

9. Figure 17.45. In the **Front UCS** create the outer flange from two cylinders (the smaller subtracted from the larger). In a similar manner create the hub, but once created a box must be subtracted to form the keyway in the hub. Then, in the **WCS** create a single spoke by extruding an ellipse. Go back the **Front UCS** and with **Array** form the six spokes for the pulley wheel. In the **WCS** position the parts correctly relative to each other and join them together with **Union**. Finally with the **Fillet** tool fillet the parts where the spokes meet the inner surface of the rim.

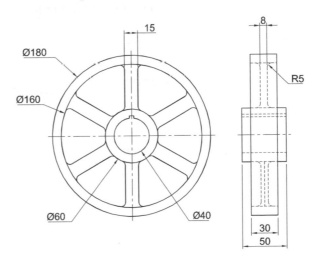

Fig. 17.46 Exercise 9 – dimensioned views

CHAPTER 18

More 3D solids

Example 1: using Fillet (Figs 18.1 and 18.2)

Figure 18.1 is a front view and plan of an engineering component. To construct a 3D model of the component:

1. Working to the dimensions given in Fig. 18.1 construct the pline outline shown at the top of Fig. 18.2.
2. **Extrude** both the outline and the circle by 30.
3. Create two cylinders each 120 high, one R60, the other R50.
4. With **Subtract**, subtract the hole from the pline outline, and the smaller cylinder from the larger.
5. Place in **UCS Front** and with **Move**, move the pipe made from two cylinders to its proper position relative to the extrusion.
6. With **Union**, union the two solids together.
7. Place in the **SW Isometric** view.
8. Call **Fillet** (this is the 2D **Fillet** tool (described on page 100) but see the note below).

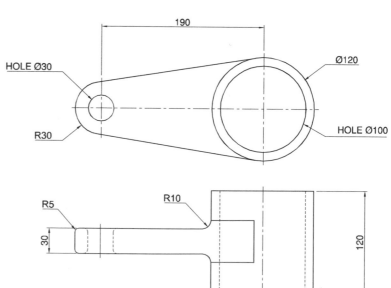

Fig. 18.1 Example 1 – dimensions

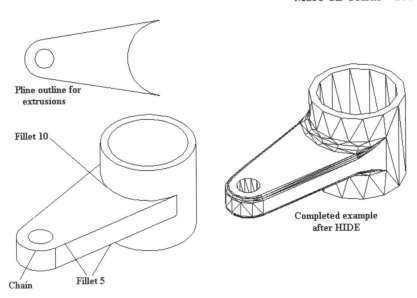

Pline outline for
extrusions

Fillet 10

Completed example
after HIDE

Fig. 18.2 Example 1 – using
Fillet

Chain   Fillet 5

Command:_fillet
(TRIM mode) Current fillet radius = 5
Polyline/Radius/Trim/<Select first object>: r (Radius)
Enter radius: 10
Command: *right-click*
(TRIM mode) Current fillet radius = 10
Polyline/Radius/Trim/<Select first object>: *pick*
Enter radius <10>: *right-click*
Chain/Radius/<Select edge>: c (Chain)
Edge/Radius/<Select edge>: *pick*
Command:

9. Repeat for the two R5 filleted edges.
10. Call **Hide**.

Note

1. If working in Release 12 the **AME** tool **Solfill** must be used for filleting edges of 3D solid models. In other releases use 2D tool **Fillet**.
2. If a series of connecting edges are to be filleted in the **Chain**, *pick* one edge after another.

Example 2: using Chamfer (Fig. 18.4)

Figure 18.3 is a dimensioned two-view drawing of the 3D solid to be created in this example.

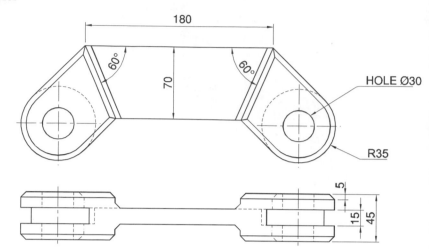

Fig. 18.3 Example 2 –
dimensions

1. With the aid of the **Polyline** tool construct the outlines of the
   central bar and one of the slotted ends (see Fig. 18.4).
2. With **Extrude**, extrude the end piece outline by 45 (including the
   circle and the bar by 15). With **Subtract** subtract the extruded
   circle from the 45-high extrusion.
3. With **Move**, move the end into position against the bar. With
   Mirror, mirror the end to produce the second end on the left-
   hand side. Create a cylinder of height 15 and radius 35 at each
   end to form the slot in the ends.
4. Place in **UCS Front**. With **Move**, move the bar and cylinders
   central to the end pieces.

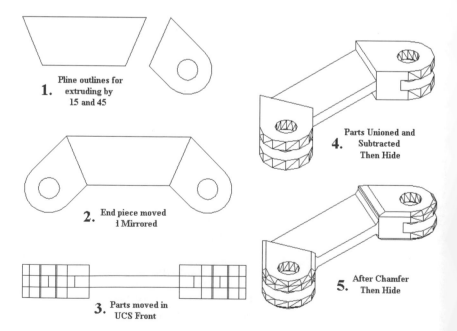

Fig. 18.4 Example 2 – using
Chamfer

5. Place in the **SW Isometric** view and with **Union**, union the bar to the ends. With **Subtract**, subtract the cylinders from the union. Call **Chamfer** (in Release 12 **Solcham**):

Command_chamfer
(TRIM mode) Current chamfer Dist 1 = 10, Dist 2 = 10
Polyline/Distance/Angle/Trim/Method/Select first line>: *pick*

6. Surface highlights. If the edge(s) to be chamfered are part of the highlighted surface *right-click*. If not *enter* **n** (Next). Continue until the correct surface highlights. Then:

Enter base surface distance <10>: 5
Enter other surface distance <10>: 5
Loop/<Select edge>: *pick* one edge of the chosen surface
Loop/<Select edge>: *pick* another edge of the chosen surface
Loop/<Select edge>: *pick* another edge of the chosen surface
Loop/<Select edge>: *right-click*
Command:

Continue until all required edges are chamfered. Then call **Hide**.

Note

1. When working in Release 12 and AutoCAD 2000 the chamfer prompts are somewhat different to those shown above, but the method of chamfering is very similar.
2. Plate IX shows a 3D model based on the second example, in which the edges have been filleted rather than chamfered.

Example 3: using Slice (Figs 18.5–18.7)

Figure 18.5 is a dimensioned two-view orthographic projection forming the basis for the 3D solid to be constructed in this example:

1. Set **ISOLINES** to **12**. Working in **UCS Front**, construct the pline outline for forming a solid of revolution.
2. Call **Revolve** and revolve the outline.
3. Call **Slice** (Fig. 18.6):

Command:_slice
Select objects: *pick* the 3D solid
Select objects: *right-click*
Slicing plane by Object/Zaxis/View/XY/YZ/ZX?<3points>: *right-click*
1st point on plane: *pick*
2nd point on plane: *pick*
3rd point on plane: *enter* .xy

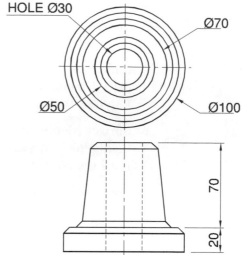

Fig. 18.5 Example 3 –
dimensions

SI
Slice

Fig. 18.6 Calling the **Slice**
tool

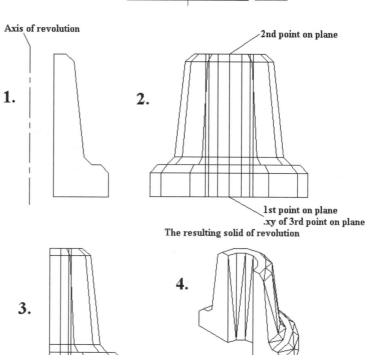

Fig. 18.7 Example 3

of: *pick* **(need Z):** *enter* 1
Both sides/<Point on desired side of plane>: *pick* the side to be
retained
Command:

4. Place the sliced 3D solid in the **NW Isometric** view.

Note

1. In Release 12 the **Slice** tool is named **Solcut**. Its action is the same as **Slice**.
2. If desired the sliced solid can be sliced again to produce say, a quarter of the original 3D solid of revolution (or any other 3D solid).

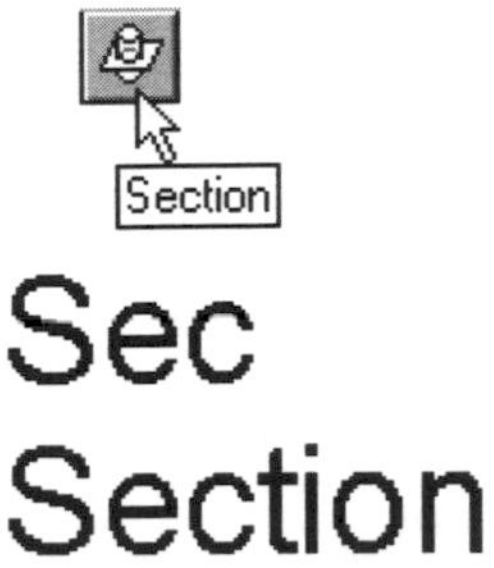

Example 4: using Section (Figs 18.8–18.12)

Figure 18.9 shows the overall dimensions for this example.

1. Figure 18.10: with **Polyline** construct an outline of the base; with **Extrude**, extrude to 40 high.
2. Figure 18.10: in **Front UCS** construct two plines as shown; extrude the two smaller outlines to 30 high and the larger to 100 high. Place the solids in **UCS Front** and with **Move**, move the parts into their correct positions relative to each other.
3. Figure 18.10: place the four parts in the **SW Isometric** view.
4. Figure 18.11: with **Subtract**, subtract the large extrusion from the base. Then with **Union**, union the two arms to the remainder of the solid.
5. Figure 18.11: in **WCS** construct an outline for the recess and with **Extrude**, extrude the outline to 10 high. Place in **UCS Front** and with **Move**, move the recess extrusion into its correct position.
6. In **WCS**, call **Section** (Fig. 18.8):

Command:_section
Select objects: *pick* the 3D model **1 found**
Select objects: *right-click*
Slicing plane by Object/Zaxis/View/XY/YZ/ZX?<3points>: *right-click*

Fig. 18.8 Calling the **Section** tool

Sec

Section

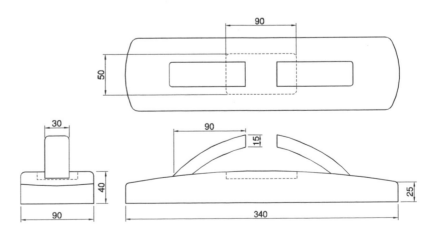

Fig. 18.9 Example 4 – front view and plan of the 3D solid

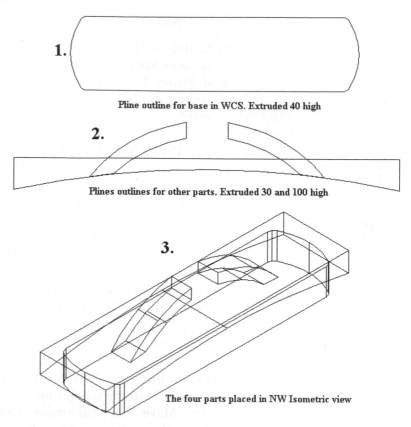

1.

Pline outline for base in WCS. Extruded 40 high

2.

Plines outlines for other parts. Extruded 30 and 100 high

3.

The four parts placed in NW Isometric view

Fig. 18.10 Example 4 –
stages 1–3

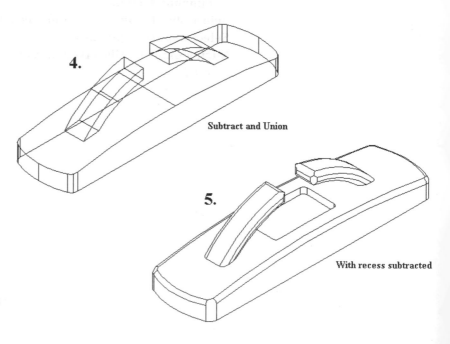

4.

Subtract and Union

5.

With recess subtracted

Fig. 18.11 Example 4 – stages
4 and 5

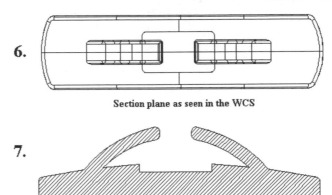

6.

Section plane as seen in the WCS

7.

Fig. 18.12 Example 4 – stages
6 and 7

The section plane after hatching

1st point on plane: *pick*
2nd point on plane: *pick*
3rd point on plane: *enter* .xy
of: *pick* **(need Z):** *enter* 1
Command:

See Fig. 18.12 which shows the section plane across the 3D
model in **WCS**.

7. Figure 18.12: the section plane outline can now be moved from
the 3D solid and hatched.

Note

If working in Release 12, the **Section** tool is called with **Solsect**.

Example 5: a more complex 3D model (Figs 18.13–18.15)

In **UCS Front**, construct outlines as shown in Fig. 18.13.

1. With **Extrude**, extrude each part of the outlines to 5 high, including the two circles. Then **Subtract** the inner outlines from
the outer.

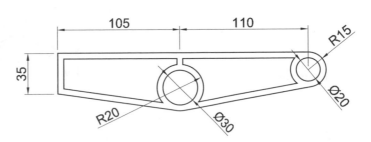

Fig. 18.13 Example 5 –
outline for first stage

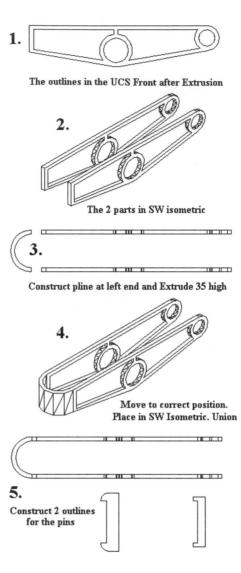

1.

The outlines in the UCS Front after Extrusion

2.

The 2 parts in SW isometric

3.

Construct pline at left end and Extrude 35 high

4.

Move to correct position.
Place in SW Isometric. Union

5.

Construct 2 outlines
for the pins

Fig. 18.14 Example 5 – stages 1–5

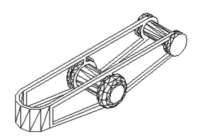

Fig. 18.15 Example 5

2. In **WCS** using **Copy**, copy the model to produce two copies 50 apart. Then place in **SW Isometric** to check.
3. Create a pline outline for the left-hand end of the model and with **Extrude**, extrude 35 high.
4. In **WCS** using **Move**, move the end into its correct position. Place the model in the **SW Isometric** view. With **Union**, union the three parts.
5. In **UCS Front**, construct two outlines for the pins.
6. Figure 18.14: with **Revolve** construct solids of revolution for the two pins. Place in **WCS** and move the pins to their correct positions. Check in **UCS Front** that they are in their correct positions.
7. Place in **SW Isometric** view and call **Hide**.

Fig. 18.16 **Tilemode UCS** icon

Example 6: Solprof (Figs 18.17–18.19)

1. With the 3D solid of Example 5 on screen call **Tilemode**:

Command: tilemode
New value for TILEMODE <0>: *enter* 1 *right-click*
Command:

The 'paper space' **UCS** icon appears at the bottom left-hand corner of the screen (Fig. 18.16). The 3D model disappears from screen.

Solprof

Fig. 18.17 Calling the **Setup Profile** tool

Command: *enter* mview *right-click*
ON/OFF/Hideplot/Fit/2/3/4/Restore/<First point>: *enter* f (Fit) *right-click*
Command: the 3D model reappears
Command: *enter* mspace *right-click*

The 'model space' **UCS** icon reappears.

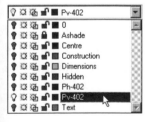

Fig. 18.18 Popup list showing layers turned off and the current layer

Fig. 18.19 Example 6 – profile-only view

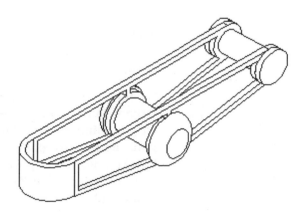

2. Call the **Setup Profile** tool (Fig. 18.17):

Command:_solprof
Select objects: *pick* one of the three objects **1 found**
Select objects: *pick* another of the three objects **1 found**
Select objects: *pick* the last of the three objects **1 found**
Select objects: *right-click*
Display hidden profile lines on separate layer <Y>: *right-click*
Project profile lines onto a plane <Y>: *right-click*
Delete tangential edges <Y>: *enter* n (No) *right-click*
3 solids selected.
Command:

3. *Click* in the **Layer Control** panel and in the popup menu which appears, turn off all layers other than the one with a name commencing 'Pv' which should be made the current layer (Fig. 18.18). The profile-only view of the example appears (Fig. 18.19).

Note

1. If the parts shown in Examples 5 and 6 had to be manufactured, each of the pins would have had to be made in two parts – because as they are shown in these examples, it would not have been possible to place them in their respective holes. These two examples therefore are showing illustrative views of the assemblies.
2. Profile-only 3D solid model drawings are similar to isometric drawings, but are in fact based upon 3D solid model drawings. The original 3D models can be seen by turning the 'Pv' layer off and the others back on.

Example 7: Slice and Section (Fig. 18.20)

Go back to the Example 3. It is possible to slice and section to show the hatched sectional outline in a 3D view.

1. Load the sliced 3D model in Fig. 18.7. Place it in **WCS**. Call **Section** and using the same **3point** plane as used for the **Slice** action, create a sectional outline (see Example 4). Then, at the command line:

Command: *enter* ucs *right-click*
Origin/ZAxis/3point/—————/<World>: *enter* 3 *right-click*
Origin point: *click* at the first point as for the section
Point on positive part of the X-axis: *click* at the second point
Point on positive-Y portion of the UCS XY plane: *enter* .xy at the
    third point **(need Z):** *enter* 1 *right-click*
Command:

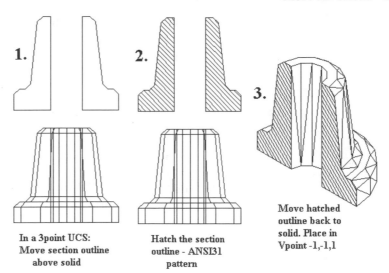

1.

2.

3.

In a 3point UCS:
Move section outline
above solid

Hatch the section
outline - ANSI31
pattern

Move hatched
outline back to
solid. Place in
Vpoint -1,-1,1

Fig. 18.20 Example 7 – **Slice** and **Section**

2. The **3point UCS** plane appears. **Move** the section outline above the solid. It can then be hatched – in this example using **ANSI31** pattern.
3. **Move** the hatched outline back to the solid and place in the **NW Isometric** view.

Note

The method of setting a new **UCS** based on a **3point** situation is useful at times when a preset **UCS** plane is not suitable for the work in hand. The **3point UCS** plane can be set at any angle within the existing **UCS** plane.

Questions

1. What is the purpose of the **Chain** prompt when using the **Fillet** tool?
2. In the 3D model examples given so far, it has been the custom to move parts into their correct positions in an appropriate **UCS** plane. It is possible to avoid having to do this by, for example, constructing outlines for extrusions using x,y,z coordinates rather than x,y coordinates. Which method would you prefer to use?
3. What is meant by '**(TRIM mode)**' in the command line prompt sequence of the **Chamfer** tool?
4. When constructing a section through a 3D solid model using the **Section** tool, it may be necessary to also **Slice** the model. Why is this so?
5. What abbreviation can be *entered* at the command line to call the **Section** tool?

6. What abbreviation can be *entered* at the command line to call the **Revolve** tool?
7. What is meant by a 'profiled' solid model?
8. Are profiled models 3D?
9. What are viewports?
10. What advantages are there in setting up profile-only drawings?

Exercises

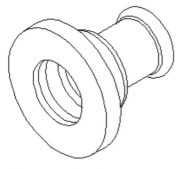

Fig. 18.21 Exercise 2

1. Open any of the 3D solid model drawings you have constructed and, with the aid of the **Setup Profile** tool, create profile-only drawings of them.
2. Figure 18.21 is a profile-only drawing of the 3D model described in the single end view in Fig. 18.22. Construct a solid of revolution to create the solid shown in Fig. 18.21 and surface profile your 3D solid model drawing.

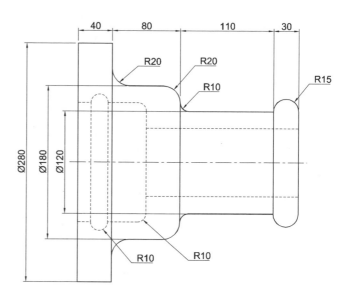

Fig. 18.22 Exercise 2 – dimensions

3. Construct the 3D solid model shown in the profile-only drawing of Fig. 18.23, working to the dimensions given in Fig. 18.24. Then surface profile your 3D solid model drawing.
4. Figure 18.25 shows a chain link in exploded and in assembled views. Figure 18.26 shows dimensions of the parts of the assembly. Construct an assembled 3D solid model of the chain link. Then slice and section the assembly.

Fig. 18.23 Exercise 3

Fig. 18.24 Exercise 3 –
dimensions

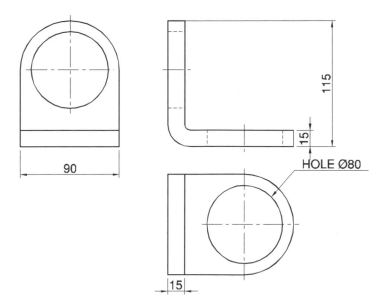

HOLE Ø80

115

15

90

15

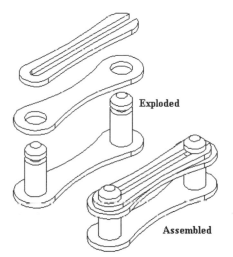

Exploded

Assembled

Fig. 18.25 Exercise 4

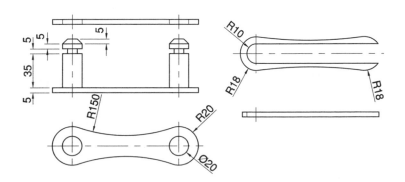

Fig. 18.26 Exercise 4 –
dimensions

5. Figure 18.27 shows an assembled profile-only drawing of the assembly described in the two-view orthographic projection Fig. 18.28. Construct the three parts of the 3D solid model drawing of the assembly and place them in the correct positions relative to each other in the assembly. Create a sliced and sectioned 3D model of the assembly showing the hatched sectioned face.

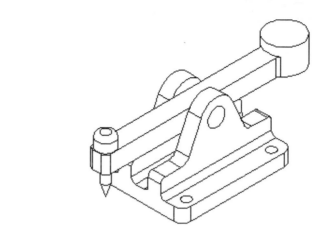

Fig. 18.27 Exercise 5

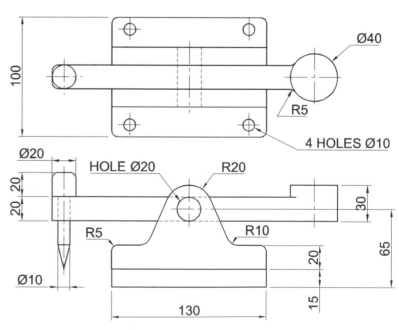

Fig. 18.28 Exercise 5 – dimensions

CHAPTER 19

Viewports

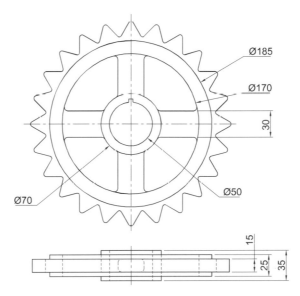

Fig. 19.1 Example 1

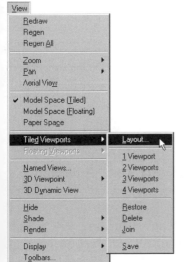

Fig. 19.2 Selecting
Layout . . . from the **View**
menu (Release 14)

Example of using viewports

Figure 19.1 is a two-view orthographic drawing. Details of the exact construction of this example are not given here, only the principles of working in a tiled viewport. The advantages of working in tiled viewports is that as the operator is working in any one viewport, different views of the 3D solid being drawn show in other viewports, lessening the possibility of making errors and making visualisation of details of the model easier as construction proceeds.

1. From the **View** menu select **Layout** . . . (Fig. 19.2). The name of this call varies between releases. In Release 12 it is **Tiled Viewports**; in AutoCAD 2000 it is **Named Viewports** . . . ; but despite differences in the dialog boxes, the meanings are the same.

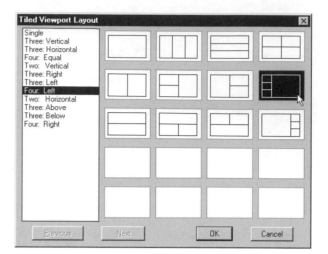

Fig. 19.3 **Tiled Viewport Layout** dialog box with **Four Left** selected

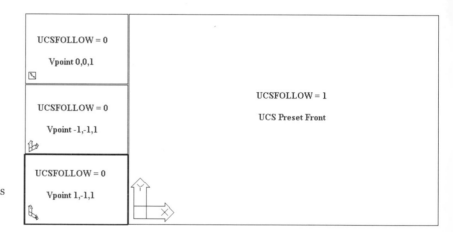

Fig. 19.4 **Four Left** viewports showing settings of **UCSFOLLOW** and **Vpoint**

2. The **Tiled Viewport Layout** dialog box (or its equivalent depending upon release) appears (Fig. 19.3). Select the layout required, in this example **Four Left**.

3. The **Four Left** viewport layout appears (Fig. 19.4). A *click* in any viewport makes that viewport the current one in which work can proceed.

4. Set up each of the four viewports as shown in Fig. 19.4, which shows the settings for **UCSFOLLOW** and for **POINT** in each of the four viewports.

5. The construction for the 3D model can now proceed. The completed model is shown in the four-viewport layout in Fig. 19.5.

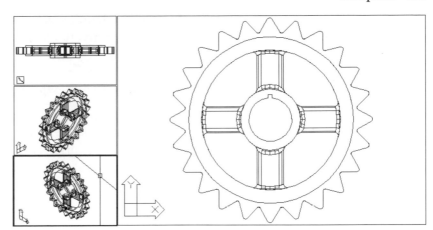

Fig. 19.5 The completed 3D model in a **Four Left** viewport

Notes

1. In the largest viewport in which **UCSFOLLOW** is set to 1, the **UCS** layout can be changed from either the **UCS Presets** dialog box or with the use of the **3point** prompt. This enables the construction of the 3D model to proceed as in the examples in this and the previous chapter. With the set variable set off in other viewports, their pictorial view does not change and as the construction proceeds the operator can look at their constructions in different views.

2. Although the use of the **Four Left** viewport layout is popular for this purpose, other layouts may be used to advantage if desired.

Model Space and Paper Space

So far, throughout this book all drawings have been constructed in 'Model Space' (**MSpace**), except for the **Solprof** example (page 241); both 2D and 3D drawings can be constructed in **MSpace**. In 'Paper Space' (**PSpace**) all drawings are in 2D; 3D drawings can be shown in **PSpace** but they are not true 3D. The advantage of working in **PSpace** is that all parts of the screen, particularly when in multiple viewports, can be printed or plotted as one drawing, whereas when working in multiple viewports in **MSpace**, only the current viewport can be printed or plotted. Some operators prefer working in **PSpace** when constructing 2D drawings, but it must be remembered that 2D drawings in this book have so far been constructed in **MSpace**.

To place the screen in **PSpace**, *enter* **tilemode** or **tm** at the command line. Changing to **PSpace** from **MSpace** can also be called by selecting the appropriate command from the **View** menu in Releases 12–14. When working in AutoCAD 2000, a *click* on one of

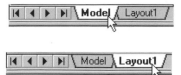

Fig. 19.6 **Model** and **Layout**
tabs (AutoCAD 2000)

the **Layout** tabs at the bottom of the AutoCAD window will switch
over to **PSpace**. Alternatively *clicking* on the **Model** tab will revert
to **MSpace** (Fig. 19.6).

Using PSpace and viewports (Figs 19.6–19.13)

This example was completed in Release 14, but the same methods
of working can be carried out when working in the other releases
covered by this book. Figure 19.7 is an isometric view of the component on which this example is based and Fig. 19.8 is a dimensioned
drawing of the component.

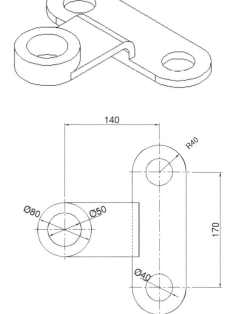

Fig. 19.7 Example 2 –
isometric view

Fig. 19.8 Example 2 –
dimensioned drawing

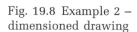

1. Construct a 3D model drawing of the component. Figure 19.9
   shows the model in **SW Isometric** view.
2. Call **Tilemode**:

   Command: tilemode
   New value for TILEMODE <1>: 0
   Command:

   The screen changes to **PSpace**.

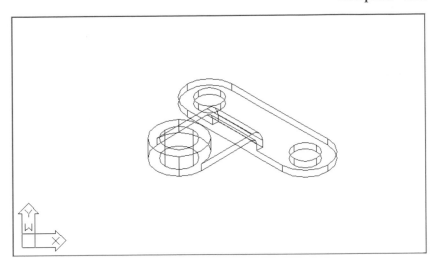

Fig. 19.9 Stage 1

3. Call **Mview**:

Command: mview
ON/OFF/Hideplot/Fit/2/3/4/Restore/<First point>: 4
Fit/<First point>: f

The screen changes to a four-viewport screen.

4. Figure 19.10: switch to **MSpace** by *entering* **ms** at the command line. Change the model drawing in each viewport to new views: top left – **Back**; top right – **Right**; bottom left – **Top**; bottom right – **SW Isometric**. **Zoom** 1 in each viewport.

5. Figure 19.11: switch back to **PSpace** by *entering* **ps** at the command line.

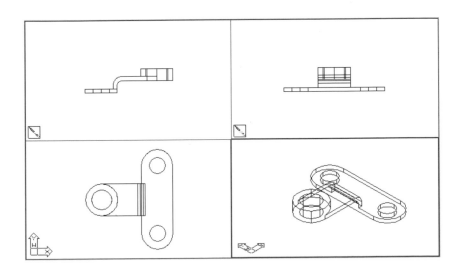

Fig. 19.10 Stage 4

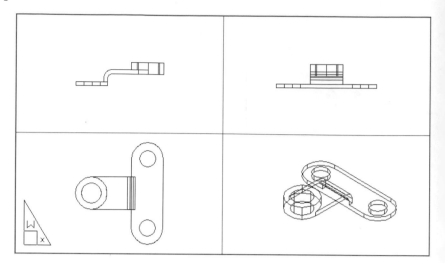

Fig. 19.11 Stage 5

6. Figure 19.12: with the aid of the **Move** tool, move each viewport as shown in Fig. 19.12. To do this call **Move** then *click* on the edge of a viewport which allows the viewport to be *dragged* to any required position.
7. Make a new layer called 'vports'. With the **Change** tool or the **Properties** tool, change the viewport outlines to the new layer.
8. Figure 19.13: turn the new layer off. The drawings on screen now appear as in Fig. 19.13, with the drawings in a three-view orthographic position plus an isometric view in the bottom right. Note that the whole screen can now be printed as it stands because it is a complete 2D drawing, derived from the original 3D construction.

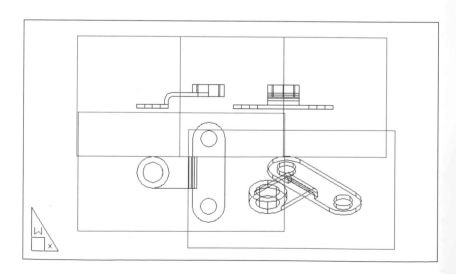

Fig. 19.12 Stage 6

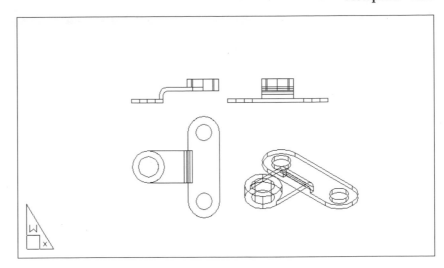

Fig. 19.13 Stage 8

Notes

1. Figure 19.14 shows the result of following the same procedures working in a Release 12 screen, using a different 3D model.

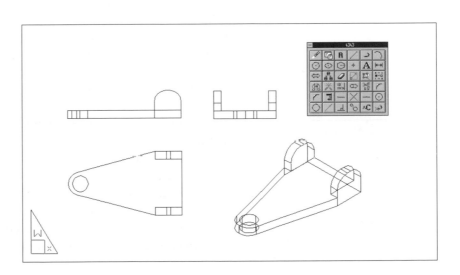

Fig. 19.14 An example completed in Release 12

2. Figure 19.15 shows the result of using the same procedures working in AutoCAD 2000 using another 3D model. Although setting **Tilemode** off has the same result in other releases, it is easier in AutoCAD 2000 to *click* on a **Layout** tab, which automatically places the drawing in a **PSpace** layout.

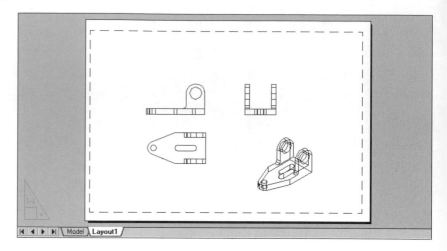

Fig. 19.15 An example
completed in AutoCAD 2000

Questions

1. Why is **Tilemode** so called?
2. What are the differences between **MSpace** and **PSpace**?
3. From the second example in this chapter it could be seen that viewports can be moved when in **PSpace**. Is this possible in **MSpace**?
4. Can viewports be erased? Can they be scaled?
5. Is it possible to use **Solprof** in each of the viewports shown in either of the examples given in this chapter?
6. How is a viewport made active (or current) when working in **MSpace**?
7. Can viewports be made separately active when working in **PSpace**?
8. Why was it necessary in the second example to change the borders of the viewports on to a different layer?
9. Why was it necessary to set **UCSFOLLOW** to 0 in some of the viewports in the first example?
10. What is the major advantage of constructing 3D solid model drawings in a two-, three- or four-viewport screen?

Exercises

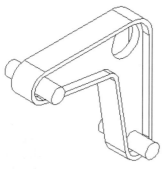

Fig. 19.16 Exercise 1 –
isometric drawing

1. Figure 19.16 shows an isometric drawing of a fitting from a link in a machine. Figure 19.17 is a dimensioned two-view orthographic projection of the fitting. Construct a 3D solid model drawing of the fitting, followed by arranging an orthographic three-view drawing in a four-viewport AutoCAD window.

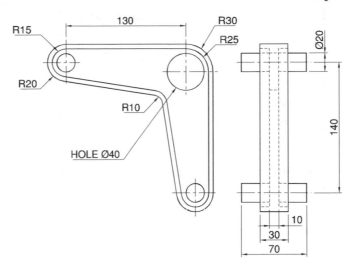

Fig. 19.17 Exercise 1 –
two-view orthographic
dimensioned drawing

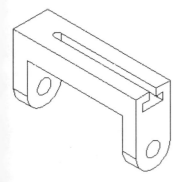

Fig. 19.18 Exercise 2 –
isometric drawing

2. Figure 19.18 is an isometric drawing of the part for this exercise
and Fig. 19.19 a three-view orthographic projection of the part
complete with dimensions. Construct a 3D solid model drawing
of the part and in a four-viewport screen. Place drawings in the
four viewports to show an orthographic projection together with
an isometric view of your 3D solid model.

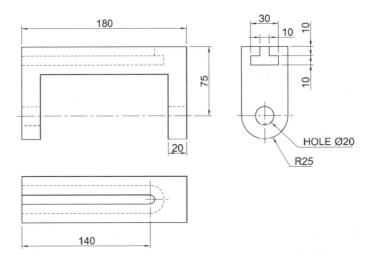

Fig. 19.19 Exercise 2 –
dimensioned three-view
orthographic projection

3. Figure 19.20 shows an isometric drawing of the 3D solid model
to be constructed for this exercise. Figure 19.21 shows dimensions for the model drawing. Construct a 3D solid model drawing of the part and then, in a four-viewport setting, adjust the
views in each viewport to resemble a three-view orthographic
projection together with an isometric view.

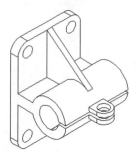

Fig. 19.20 Exercise 3 –
isometric drawing

Fig. 19.21 Exercise 3 – two-
view orthographic projection

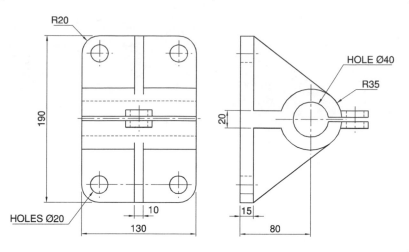

4. Figure 19.22 shows an isometric drawing of the 3D model for
this exercise and Fig. 19.23 gives a two-view orthographic projection with dimensions for the model. Construct the 3D model
and, in a four-viewport setting, adjust the views in the viewports
to produce a three-view orthographic projection of the solid
model.

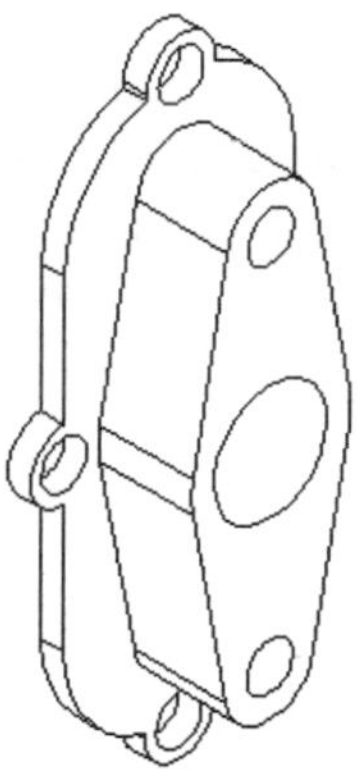

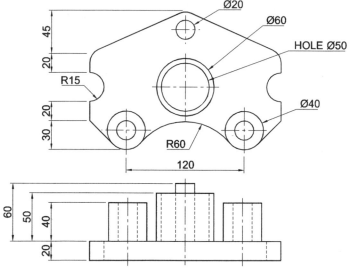

Fig. 19.22 Exercise 4 –
isometric drawing

Fig. 19.23 Exercise 4 – two-
view orthographic projection

CHAPTER 20

Rendering

Introduction

A number of the colour plates in this book show 3D solid model drawings which have been rendered. Rendering is a system which produces photo-realistic coloured images from 3D solid model drawings. Rendering in AutoCAD usually follows a sequence such as:

1. A 3D solid model drawing is constructed.
2. The model is placed in a suitable **UCS** plane to allow lights to be included for illuminating the model.
3. Colours or textures are added to the model to give an appearance of having been made from the real materials.
4. The model is placed in a suitable viewing position.
5. The model is then rendered. Backgrounds can be included in the rendering if required.

Rendering tools are available in Release 12 providing the AME software has been loaded. Figure 20.1 shows the AME menu.

With Release 13 (and later releases) the rendering tools have been included within the main software. The details given in this chapter deal with the rendering of 3D models in Releases 13, 14 and AutoCAD 2000.

Fig. 20.1 **Render** menu (Release 12)

The Render toolbars

Figure 20.2 shows the **Render** toolbars. Although these three toolbars show some variation, only the four tools shown in Fig. 20.3, taken from the Release 14 **Render** toolbar, will be dealt with in this chapter.

Example 1: rendering (Figs 20.4–20.15)

1. Construct a 3D solid model drawing of the component shown in the dimensioned two-view orthographic projection in Fig. 20.4. Figure 20.5 is an isometric drawing of the solid model.
2. Place the solid model drawing in **WCS**, **Zoom** to a suitable scale and move towards the top of the screen.

Release 13

Release 14

AutoCAD 2000

Fig. 20.2 **Render** toolbars
(Releases 13 and
14/AutoCAD 2000)

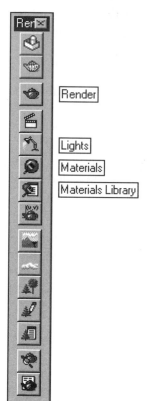

Render

Lights

Materials

Materials Library

Fig. 20.3 **Render** tools with
which this chapter is
concerned

Fig. 20.4 Example 1 –
dimensioned orthographic
projection

3. *Click* on the **Lights** tool icon in the **Render** toolbar. The **Lights**
   dialog box appears (Fig. 20.5). Ensure **Point Light** is showing in
   the popup list next to the **New ...** button. *Click* on the **New ...**
   button. The **New Point Light** dialog box appears (Fig. 20.6).
4. In the **New Point Light** dialog box, *enter* **PO1** in the **Light Name:**
   box, followed by a *click* in the **Shadow On** checkbox, then
   again on the **Modify<** button. At the command line:

Command:_lights
Enter light location: *enter* .xy *right-click*
of 140,290
(need Z): 250
Command:

The dialog box reappears. *Click* on the **OK** button.

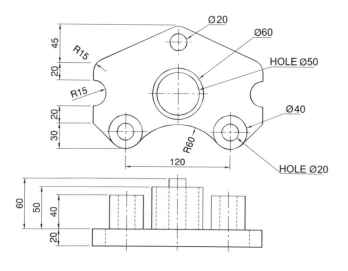

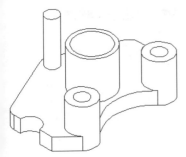

Fig. 20.5 Example 1 –
isometric drawing

Fig. 20.6 **Lights** dialog box

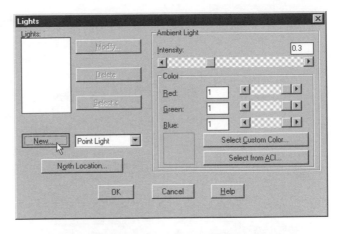

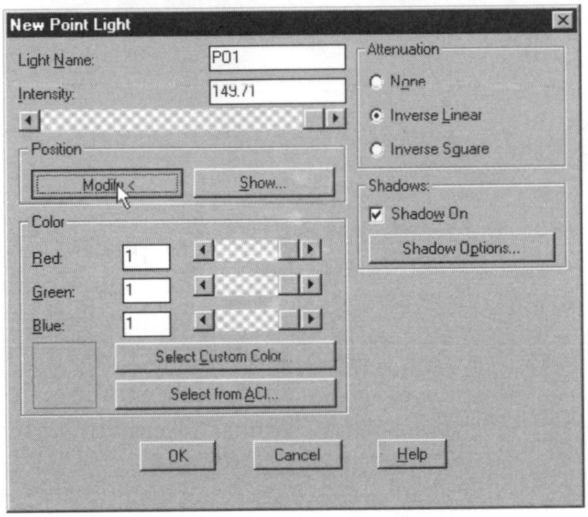

Fig. 20.7 **New Point Light**
dialog box

5. The **Lights** dialog box reappears. Change the name in the popup
   list to **Distant Light** and *click* on the **New . . .** button. The **New
   Distant Light** dialog box appears (Fig. 20.8).

6. In this dialogue box *enter* **DO1** in the **Light Name:** box and
   click in the **Shadow On** checkbox, followed by another *click* on
   the **Modify<** button. The command line shows:

   Command:_lights
   Enter light direction TO<current>: *enter* .xy *right-click*
   of *left-click* at the centre of the 3D model plan
   (need Z): 50
   Enter light direction FROM<current>: *enter* .xy *right-click*
   of 330,-100
   (need Z): 300
   Command:

   The dialog box reappears. *Click* on its **OK** button.

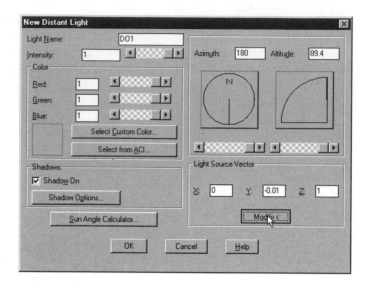

Fig. 20.8 **New Distant Light**
dialog box

7. Repeat to place a second distant light in a similar manner. When the **Lights** dialog box appears after placing the second distant light, *click* on the dialog box's **OK** button. The screen now shows three light icons as indicated in Fig. 20.9. Note that in this illustration, the lights icons have been enlarged by 50 times. This is to show the positions of the lights clearly in the illustration.

Point light at
140,-100,300

Fig. 20.9 Position of the three
lights in relation to the 3D
solid model

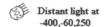 Distant light at
-400,-60,250

Ditsnt light at
330,-100,300

8. *Click* on the **Materials Library** tool icon in the **Render** toolbar. The **Materials Library** dialog box appears (Fig. 20.10). In the **Library List** select the material **GOLD2**, followed by a *click* on the **Import<** button. The name **GOLD2** then appears in the **Materials List**. *Click* on this name and again on the **Preview** button. A preview of the material appears in the preview box. If satisfied, *click* on the **OK** button of the dialog box.

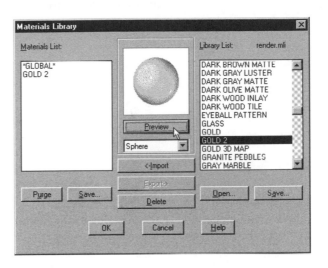

Fig. 20.10 **Materials Library** dialog box

9. *Click* on the **Materials** tool icon from the **Render** toolbar. The **Materials** dialog box appears (Fig. 20.11). *Click* on the **GOLD2** name, followed by another on the **Attach<** button. The dialog box disappears. The command line shows:

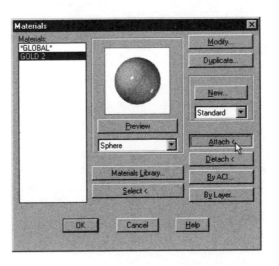

Fig. 20.11 **Materials** dialog box

Command:_rmat
Select objects to attach "GOLD2" to: *pick* the 3D solid
Select objects: *right-click*
Updating objects . . . done
Command:

10. Place the 3D solid in a suitable viewing position. Figure 20.12 shows the solid in **NW Isometric** 1 view with the three scaled-up light icons showing.

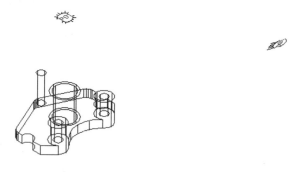

Fig. 20.12 The 3D solid with the light icons in a viewing position

11. **Zoom** the model only to a larger size and *click* on the **Render** tool icon in the **Render** toolbar. The **Render** dialog box appears (Fig. 20.13). In the **Rendering Type:** popup list select **Photo Raytrace**. Then *click* on the **More Options . . .** button to bring

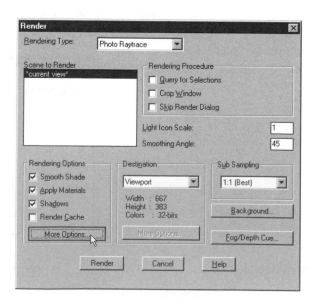

Fig. 20.13 **Render** dialog box

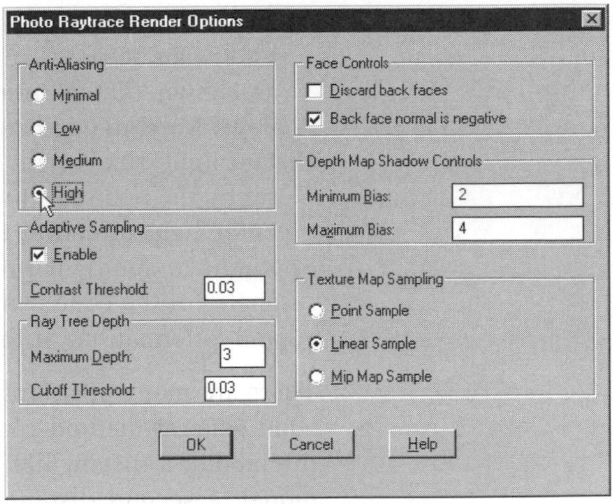

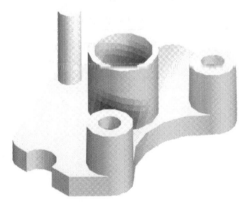

Fig. 20.14 **Photo Raytrace Render Options** dialog box

up **Photo Raytrace Render Options** dialog box (Fig. 20.14). In this dialogue box ensure that the **High** radio button is set 'on' in the **Anti-aliasing** list. *Click* on the **OK** button of the dialog box, which brings back the **Render** dialog box.

12. In this dialog box, make sure that the **Smooth Shade**, **Materials** and **Shadows** checkboxes are set 'on', then *click* on the **Render** button. The dialog box disappears and the 3D solid model is rendered (Fig. 20.15).

13. If not satisfied with the rendering materials and lights can be amended until a satisfactory rendering is obtained.

Fig. 20.15 The rendering

Notes

1. Four types of lighting are available when rendering:

   Ambient light, usually set at 30: this is the light that is always all around us and is shed in all directions.

Point light: sheds light in all directions from the source of the light. Can be set as required to any of the available strengths as shown in the **Intensity** box, with its slider in the **New Point Light** dialog box.

Distant light: sheds light in one direction only – in the direction set by the operator (prompts are **Enter light direction TO** and **Enter light direction FROM.**)

Spotlight: a spotlight produces a beam of light in a cone, the angles of the cone can be changed together with the 'hotspot' and 'attenuation' of the cone of light.

2. There are many positions for lights. The example above shows a good general method of positioning lights: a point light above the model; a distant light at the front, set at a height above the model; a second distant light at a lower intensity set to point from the left or right and at a height above the model.

3. Further lights can be added as required. One light position which can produce good effects is behind and below the model being illuminated.

4. The intensity of any of the lights, including the ambient lighting, can be amended in the appropriate dialog boxes.

Example 2: rendering (Figs 20.16–20.20)

This example has been constructed in AutoCAD 2000. However the same methods are appropriate to the other releases described in this book. Figure 20.16 is an isometric view of the 3D model to be rendered in this example and Fig. 20.17 shows a dimensioned orthographic projection of the model.

1. Construct the 3D model and place it in **WCS**. **Zoom** to a suitable scale to allow lighting to be added.

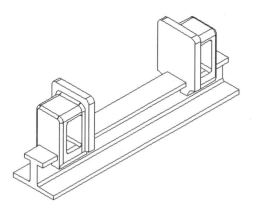

Fig. 20.16 Example 2 – isometric view

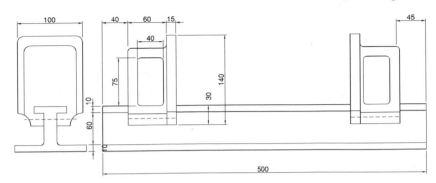

Fig. 20.17 Example 2 –
dimensioned orthographic
projection

2. Add lights as shown in Fig. 20.18. Spotlights are added in a similar manner as distant lights. When adding the spotlight accept the default values for hotspot, falloff and attenuation.
3. Place the scene including model and lights in a suitable viewing position. Figure 20.19 shows the model with lights in **SW Isometric** view.

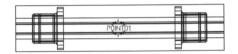

Point light at 250,200,500

Fig. 20.18 The position of the
three lights

Distant light at
-280,250,300

Spotlight at
550,-270,500

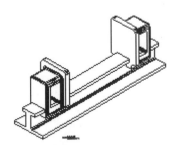

Fig. 20.19 The model with
lights in **SW Isometric** view

4. Window **Zoom** the model only.
5. Add materials: in this example the two materials COPPER (movable parts) and OLIVE METAL (bar) were attached to the three parts of the model.
6. Render the model using **Photo Raytrace** rendering with **Anti-aliasing** set high. The result is shown in Fig. 20.20.
7. A colour plate of this rendering is given in Plate XV.

Fig. 20.20 Example 2 – the rendering

Questions

1. What is meant by the term 'rendering' as applied to CAD work?
2. What is 'ambient' light?
3. What is the difference between a point light and a distant light?
4. What is the difference between a distant light and a spotlight?
5. Although not dealt with in this chapter, have you attempted placing a background to a rendering? (See Plate IX.)

Exercises

Load any of the 3D models you have constructed as worked examples or as exercises and render each in turn.

APPENDIX A

The Internet

Introduction

Release 14 and AutoCAD 2000 both include features for accessing the Internet to obtain up-to-date help information and for sending and receiving drawings files. The help information for these releases can be accessed by *clicking* on **Help** in the menu bar, then *clicking* **Connect to Interent** (Release 14) or **AutoCAD on the Web** (AutoCAD 2000) followed by selecting from the sub-menu which appears (Fig. A.1). The same facilities are available in later releases of AutoCAD LT. In both AutoCAD releases drawings can also be sent or received over the Internet.

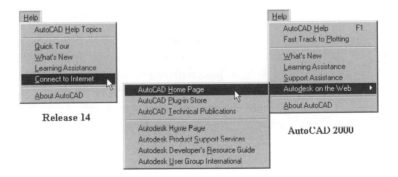

Fig. A.1 Connecting to the Internet (Release 14/ AutoCAD 2000)

HTML

HTML (hypertext markup language) is a standard formatting language designed for creating pages which can be sent or received via the Web and viewed in web browsers such as Netscape Navigator or Internet Explorer. Setting up a server is expensive for a single user of AutoCAD; space can, however, be rented from internet service providers (ISPs).

Although the HTML language can be easily learned and is quite straightforward, it is beyond the scope of this book to describe the language and how webpages can be created.

URLs

A URL (uniform resource locator) is the address of a computer server to and from which files (such as AutoCAD drawings) can be sent or received. In order to be able to do this you will need a computer equipped with a web browser and an internet connection. It is advisable to have the latest version of your browser installed in order to obtain the best results.

A URL consists of three parts. For example:

http://www.autodesk.com/acaduser

- **http** is the service 'protocol' which defines how information is sent and received.
- **www.autodesk.com** is the main Internet address of the website or server being accessed.
- **acaduser** is the location at the website or server of a specific webpage or file.

Another common protocol is **ftp** (there are a few others). When sending or receiving AutoCAD drawings over the Internet the **ftp** protocol is usually used because this protocol is designed to handle large files (such as AutoCAD drawings) more efficiently than the **http** protocol.

Internet security

In order to ensure privacy it is necessary to use passwords to protect what is sent or received over the Internet. Requests for passwords are often encountered on the Web. When typing in a password, the letters or numbers will show in the password entry box as asterisks, further guarding against anybody 'overlooking' learning your password.

Note

A special AutoCAD drawing format ***.dwf** is used for sending and receiving drawings over the Internet.

Sending and receiving drawing files

Figure A.2 is a diagram showing how the design office of a construction firm based in England can send drawings to and from various teams working on projects all over the world. The central design office and each of the teams working away from the central office are equipped with computer servers for sending and receiving drawing files via the Internet using the ftp protocol. The drawings can be sent/received in a very short period of time and this

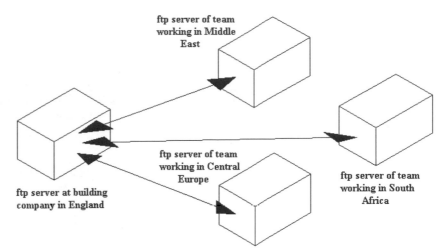

Fig. A.2 Sending and
receiving drawing files

facility is particularly effective when modifications to existing drawings are required or when teams away from the home office wish to query drawings and be sent modifications if needed.

It is beyond the scope of this book to describe the sending and receiving of drawings over the Internet, but it is simple to obtain AutoCAD help over the Web. Figures A.3–A.5 show the help pages called when **AutoCAD Home Page** is selected for the **Help** menu in AutoCAD 2000 (as shown in Fig. A.1). Figure A.6 shows the help page for AutoCAD LT 98.

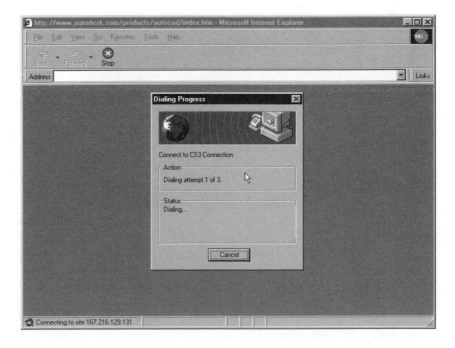

Fig. A.3 **Dial-up Connection**
dialog box

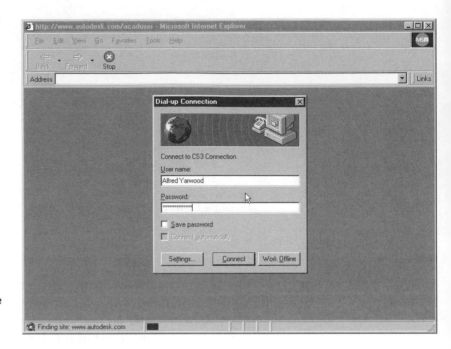

Fig. A.4 *Entering* **User Name**
and **Password** to obtain
access to the Internet

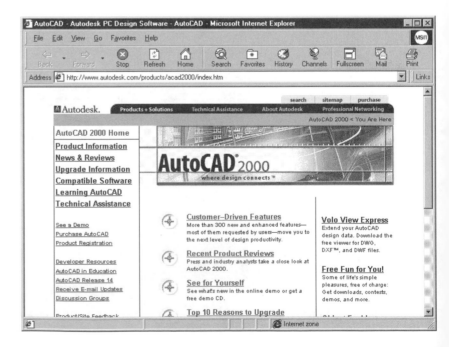

Fig. A.5 The AutoCAD 2000
Homepage

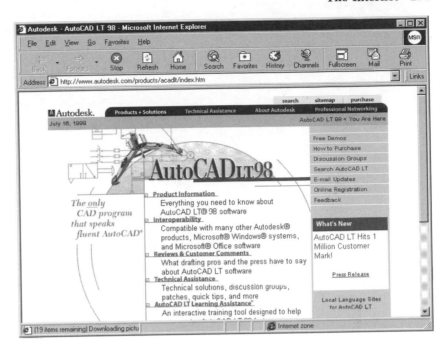

Fig. A.6 The LT 98
Homepage

Set variables

Introduction

AutoCAD is controlled by a large number of set variables, many of which are automatically set when making entries in dialog boxes. Many are also automatically set depending upon the configuration of the particular AutoCAD release.

Below is a list of those set variables which can be set by *entering* characters at the command line. To set a variable, enter its name at the command line and respond to the prompts which are seen.

To see all the set variables, *enter* **set** (or **setvar**) at the command line:

Command: *enter* set *right-click*
SETVAR Enter variable name or ?: *enter* ? *right-click*
Enter variable name to list <*>: *right-click*

A text window opens showing part of a list of all variables; to view the rest of the list press the **Return** key when prompted.

ANGDIR   Sets angle direction: **0** counterclockwise; **1** clockwise.
APERTURE   Sets size of pick box in pixels.
BLIPMODE   Sets marker blips: **1** blips show; **0** no blips.
CMDDIA   Set to **1** enables **Plot** dialog box; set to **0** disables **Plot** dialog box.

   DIM variables: there are 50–60 variables related to dimensioning, but most are set in the **Dimension Styles** dialog box or as dimensioning proceeds. However one series of **DIM** variables may be of interest:

DIMBLK   Sets a name for the block drawn for an operator's own arrowheads; these are drawn in unit sizes and saved as required.
DIMBLK1   Operator's arrowhead for beginning of line.
DIMBLK2   Operator's arrowhead for end of line.

DRAGMODE   Sets dragging: **0** no dragging; **1** dragging on; **2** automatic dragging

DRAGP1   Sets regeneration drag sampling; initial value is **10**.

DRAGP2   Sets fast dragging regeneration rate; initial value is **25**.

EDGEMODE (not in Release 12)   Controls the use of **Trim** and **Extend**: **0** does not use extension mode, **1** uses extension mode.

FILEDIA   Sets dialog boxes: **0** disables dialog boxes; **1** enables dialog boxes.

FILLMODE   Set to **0** entities created with **Solid** are not filled; set to **1** they are filled.

MIRRTEXT   Set to **0** text direction is retained; set to **1** text is mirrored.

PELLIPSE (only Release 14/AutoCAD 2000)   Set to **0** creates true ellipses; set to **1** polyline ellipses.

PICKBOX   Sets selection pick box height in pixels.

PICKDRAG   Set to **0** selection windows picked by two corners; set to **1** selection windows are dragged from corner to corner.

QTEXTMODE   Set to **0** turns off Quick Text; set to **1** enables Quick Text.

SAVETIME   Sets autosave time: initially **120**; set to **0** disables autosave.

SHADEDGE   Set to **0** faces are shade, edges are not highlighted; set to **1** faces are shaded, edges in colour of entity; set to **2** faces are not shaded, edges in entity colour; set to **3** faces in entity colour, edges in background colour.

SHORTCUTMENU (only in AutoCAD 2000)   For controlling how *right-click* menus show: **0** all disabled; **1** default menus only; **2** edit mode menus; **4** command mode menus; **8** command mode menus only when options are currently available. Add the variable settings to set multiple options.

SKETCHINC   Sets the **Sketch** record increment; initial value is **0.1**.

SKPOLY   Set to **0** and **Sketch** makes line; set to **1** and **Sketch** makes polylines.

SURFTAB1   Sets mesh density in the M direction for surfaces generated with the **Surfaces** tools.

SURFTAB2   Sets mesh density in the N direction for surfaces generated with the **Surfaces** tools.

TEXTFILL (not in Release 12)   Set to **0** TrueType text shows as outlines only; set to **1** TrueType text is filled.

TILEMODE   Sets tiled viewports: **0** Paper Space enabled; **1** Model Space.

TOOLTIPS (only Release 14/AutoCAD 2000)   Set to **0** no tooltips; set to **1** tooltips enabled.

TRIMMODE (not in Release 12)   Set to **0** edges not trimmed when **Chamfer** and **Fillet** are used; set to **1** edges are trimmed.

UCSFOLLOW   Set to **0** new UCS settings do not take effect; set to **1** UCS settings follow requested settings.

UCSICON   Set to **0** and the UCS icon does not show; set to **1** and it shows.

Glossary of computer terms

Application – The name given to software packages which perform the tasks such as word processing, desktop publishing, CAD etc.

ASCII – American national standard code for information interchange. A code which sets bits for characters used in computing.

Attribute – Text appearing in a drawing, sometimes linked to a block.

Autodesk – The American company which produces AutoCAD and other CAD software packages.

Baud rate – A measure of the rate at which a computer system can receive information (measured in bits per second).

BIOS – Basic input-output system. The chip in a PC that controls the operations performed by the hardware (e.g. disks, screen, keyboard etc.).

Bit – Short for binary digit. Binary is a form of mathematics that uses only two numbers: 0 and 1. Computers operate completely on binary mathematics.

Block – A group of objects or entities on screen that have been linked together to act as one unit.

Booting up – Starting up a computer to an operating level.

Bus – An electronic channel that allows the movement of data around a computer.

Byte – A sequence of 8 bits.

C – A computer programming language.

Cache – A section of memory (can be ROM or RAM) which holds data that is being frequently used. Speeds up the action of disks and applications.

CAD – Computer-aided design. The term should not be used to mean computer aided drawing.

CAD/CAM – Computer-aided design and manufacturing;

CD-ROM – Computer disc read only memory. A disk system capable of storing several hundred Mbytes of data – commonly 640 Mbytes.

Chips – Pieces of silicon (usually) that drive computers, and into which electronic circuits are embedded.

Command line – In AutoCAD 2000, the command line is in a window in which commands are entered from the keyboard and which contains the prompts and responses to commands.

Clock speed – Usually measured in MHz (Megaherz) – this is the measure of the speed at which a computer processor works.

CMOS – Complimentary metal oxide semiconductor. Often found as battery-powered chips which control features such as the PC's clock-speed.

Communications – Describes the software and hardware that allow computers to communicate.

Coprocessor – A processor chip in a computer which runs in tandem with the main processor chip and can deal with arithmetic involving many decimal points (floating-point arithmetic). Often used in CAD systems to speed up drawing operations.

CPU – Central processing unit. The chip that drives a PC.

Data – Information that is created, used or stored on a computer in digital form.

Database – A piece of software that can handle and organise large amounts of information.

Dialog box – A window that appears on screen in which options may be presented to the user, or requires the user to input information requested by the current application.

Directories – The system in MS-DOS for organising files on disk. Could be compared with a folder (the directory) containing documents (the files).

Disks – Storage hardware for holding data (files, applications etc.). There are many types: the most common are hard disks (for mass storage) and floppy disks (less storage) and CD-ROMs (mass storage).

Display – The screen allowing an operator to see the results of his work at a computer.

DOS – Disk operating system. The software that allows the computer to access and organise stored data. MS-DOS (produced by the Microsoft Corporation) is the DOS most widely used in PCs.

DTP – Desktop publishing. DTP software allows for the combination of text and graphics into page layouts which may then be printed.

Entity – A single feature in graphics being drawn on screen – a line, a circle, a point. Sometimes linked together in a block, when the block acts as an entity.

EMS – Expanded memory specification. RAM over and above the original limit of 640 Kbytes RAM in the original IBM PC. PCs are now being built to take up to 128 Mb RAM (or even more).

File – Collection of data held as an entity on a disk.

Fixed disk – A hard disk that cannot usually be easily removed from the computer as distinct from floppy disks which are designed to be easily removable.

Floppy disk – A removable disk that stores data in magnetic form. The actual disk is a thin circular sheet of plastic with a magnetic surface, hence the term 'floppy'. It usually has a firm plastic case.

Flyout – A number of extra tool icons which appear when a tool icon that shows a small arrow is selected from a toolbar.

Formatting – The process of preparing the magnetic surface of a disk to enable it to hold digital data.

ftp – File transfer protocol. An internet protocol used to fetch a required resource from a web server.

Giga – Means 1,000,000,000. In computer memory terms really 1,000 Mb (megabytes) – actually 1,073,741,824 bytes because there are 1024 bytes in a kilobyte (Kb).

GUI – Graphical user interface. Describes software (such as Windows) which allows the user to control the computer by representing functions with icons and other graphical images.

Hardcopy – The result of printing (or plotting) text or graphics on to paper or card.

Hard disk – A disk, usually fixed in a computer, which rotates at high speed and will hold large amounts of data (measured in gigabytes).

Hardware – The equipment used in computing: the computer itself, disks, printers, monitor etc.

HTML – Hypertext markup language. A computer language for setting up pages which can be viewed over the web.

http – Hypertext transfer protocol. An internet protocol used to fetch a required resource from a web server.

Hz (hertz) – The measure of 1 cycle per second. In computing terms, often used in millions of hertz – (megahertz or MHz) as a measure of the clock speed.

IBM – International Business Machines. An American computer manufacturing company.

Intel – An American company which manufactures the processing chips used in many PCs.

Internet – A network of computers linked in a world-wide system.

Joystick – A small control unit used mainly in computer games. Some CAD systems use a joystick to control drawing on screen.

Kilo – Means 1000. In computing terms 1K (kilobyte) is 1024 bytes.

LAN – Local area network. Describes a network that typically link PCs in an office by cable where distances between the PCs is small.

Library – A set of frequently used symbols, phrases or other data on disk, that can be easily accessed by the operator.

Light pen – Used as a stylus to point directly at a display screen sensitive to its use.

Memory – Any medium (such as RAM or ROM chips), that allows the computer to store data internally that can be instantly recalled.

Message box – A window containing a message to be acted on which appears in response when certain tools or command are selected.

MHz – Megahertz – 1,000,000 hertz (cycles per second).

Mouse – A device for controlling the position of an on-screen cursor within a GUI such as Windows.

Microsoft – The American company which produces Windows and other software.

Mips – Millions of instructions per second. A measure of a computer's speed – it is not comparable with the clock speed as measured in MHz, because a single instruction may take more than a cycle to perform.

Monitor – Display screen.

Multitasking – A computer that can carry out more than one task at a time is said to said to be multitasking. For example in AutoCAD for Windows printing can be carried out 'in the background' while a new drawing is being constructed.

Multiuser – A computer that may be used by more than one operator.

Networking – The joining together of a group of computers allowing them to share the same data and software. LANs and WANs are examples of the types of networks available.

Object – A term used in CAD to describe an entity or group of entities that have been linked together.

Operating system – Software that allows the user to operate applications software and organise and use data stored on a computer.

PC – Personal computer.

Pixels – The individual dots on a monitor display.

Plotter – Produces hardcopy of, for instance, a drawing produced on a computer by moving a pen over a piece of paper or card.

Printer – There are many types of printer: bubble-jet and laser are the most common. Allows material produced on a computer (graphics and text) to be output as hardcopy.

Processor – The operating chip of a PC. Usually a single chip, such as the Intel Pentium.

Programs – A set of instructions to the computer that has been designed to produce a given result.

RAM – Random access memory. Data stored in RAM is lost when the computer is switched off, unless previously saved to a disk.

RGB – Red, green, blue.

ROM – Read only memory. Refers to those chips from which the data stored can be read, but to which data cannot be written. The data on a ROM is not lost when a computer is switched off.

Scanner – Hardware capable of being passed over a document or drawing and reading the image into a computer.

Software – Refers to any program or application that is used and run on a computer.

SQL – Structured query language. A computer programming language for translating and transferring data between an application such as AutoCAD and a database.

Tools – Tools, are usually selected from icons appearing in toolbars. A tool represents a command.

Toolbar – Toolbars contain a number of icons, representing tools.

Tooltip – When a tool is selected by a *left-click* on its icon, a small box appears (a tooltip) carrying the name of the tool.

UNIX – A multiuser, multitasking operating system (short for UNICS: uniplexed information and computing systems).

URL – Uniform resource locator. Web addresses are examples of URLs.

VDU – Visual display unit.

Vectors – Refers to entities in computer graphics which are defined by the coordinates of end points of each part of the entity.

Virtual memory – A system by which disk space is used as if it were RAM to allow the computer to function as if more physical RAM were present. It is used by AutoCAD (and other software) but can slow down a computer's operation.

WAN – Wide area network. A network of computers that are a large distance apart – often communicating by telephone.

Warning box – A window containing a warning or request which the user must respond to, which appears when certain circumstances are met or actions are made.

WIMP – Windows, icons, mice and pointers. A term used to describe some GUIs.

Window – An area of the computer screen within which applications such as word processors may be operated.

Workstation – Often used to refer to a multiuser PC, or other system used for the purposes of CAD (or other applications).

WORM – Write once read many. An optical data storage system that allows blank optical disks to have data written onto them only once.

www – world-wide web.

WYSIWYG – What you see is what you get. What is seen on the screen is what will be printed.

Index